THE
BOARD GAME

Praise for

THE BOARD GAME

"*The Board Game* is an excellent and cautionary tale for heads of schools unfamiliar with the nature of 'the governance game,' and an excellent and engaging lesson cloaked in the drama of fiction that hits, sadly, too close to home."

Patrick F. Bassett
President, NAIS—National Association of Independent Schools

"The relationship between the head of school and the board of trust is the fulcrum upon which excellence and mediocrity in independent and private schools rest. An unhealthy relationship between the two set an unexceptional and uninspiring glass ceiling on a school and its culture; whereas, best-practices and healthy relationships set the school and its culture on a trajectory for excellence. In his book *The Board Game*, William Mott highlights this truth through engaging and accessible prose. This is a must read for both the experienced, as well hopeful, head of school, and it ought to be a part of every board of trust orientation."

Ken Cheeseman
Head of School for St. Paul Christian Academy (Nashville, TN)

"William Mott's style of insightful prose adds a personal perspective to the sometimes dry topic of governance. *The Board Game* talks about the real issues we all face in the field everyday as opposed to the idealistic way some authors suppose the world to be. If you have ever been a leader in such settings, you will find these scenarios achingly familiar and the responses thought-provoking."

Kim Carpenter Drake
Vice President, Center for Nonprofit Management

"*The Board Game* gives insight into the art and science of leadership and governance through the real twists and turns that are inevitable realities of organizational life. In a refreshing story format, William Mott places guiding principles for successfully navigating partnerships in plain sight so leaders can reach mission effectiveness. Dr. Mott's great ability to connect has become a conduit for the breadth of his experience, leadership, and tangible insight in *The Board Game*. This is a recommended resource for those seriously seeking to achieve success through the best assets of a board and wise governance, coupled with the finest execution of fitting and timely leadership."

Dr. Brad Gray
President and CEO at Peabody Global Group and
Former Vice President, NAIS—National Association
of Independent Schools

"Every independent school leader and board member should read *The Board Game*. William Mott provides an easy-to-read resource on board leadership. Drawing from many leaders' experiences in independent schools and nonprofit organizations, Dr. Mott writes an inspiring and thought-provoking fictional portrayal of a board's relationship, responsibility, and role to the institution and administrator. While the characters are not real, the experiences are lived out in schools and non-profits every day. This should be required reading for every school and nonprofit leader today in order to avoid some of the mistakes and missteps depicted in *The Board Game*. Through Dr. Mott's expertise, insight, and creativity, organizations will now have better direction for their boards."

Dr. Rick Newberry
President of Enrollment Catalyst (Seminole, FL)

"With the dramatic changes in the economy, private corporations along with faith-based, educational, and nonprofit organizations face extraordinary challenges to manage through these turbulent times. Those that will survive and thrive in the coming years will be organizations where the leadership and the board work collaboratively so that their energy and attention are focused on addressing external issues rather than internal ones. William Mott uses his vast experience to creatively guide his readers to a better understanding of how to build that internal partnership between board and leadership. Any leader working directly with a board of directors will find *The Board Game* extremely eye-opening and Dr. Mott's insight highly beneficial."

Danny Herron
President and CEO of Habitat for Humanity of Greater Nashville

"William Mott is an experienced leader and thoughtful educator. *The Board Game* reflects the kind of substantive intellectual capacity that Dr. Mott brings to life, and it offers practical insights and critical skills that will be of help to any leader whose success depends largely on a partnership with volunteer boards. He brings a lifetime of experience and reflection to bear on this new book, and I commend it to all who wish to keep growing as leaders."

Dr. Todd Jones
Senior Pastor, First Presbyterian Church—Nashville, Tennessee

"Whatever your stage of the game, you will gain insight and perspective from *The Board Game*. While focused on independent schools, William Mott's lessons will resonate with every non-profit organization that is driven by a governing board. This will undoubtedly become one of the few well-worn books I reread regularly as my own professional journey continues."

Kasey Anderson
Executive Director of the Nashville Academy of Medicine

"Understanding the intuitive and counter-intuitive aspects of leadership is tricky business in simple organizations. It takes on monumental subtlety and importance in complex nonprofit institutions. *The Board Game* accurately captures the joys and heartaches of the working relationship between the paid, professional leader and the volunteer, board-member leader. Both types of leadership—governance and management—are vital to the health of the nonprofit organization. Success demands the best of everyone involved: superb emotional intelligence, practiced communication skills, and a deep wellspring of good will. If you're ready for a wild ride through the untamed frontier of nonprofit leadership, Dr. Mott is ready and imminently qualified to be your guide."

Dr. John Cooper
Headmaster of TMI—The Episcopal School of Texas

"The landscape of nonprofit organizations, including colleges and universities, is a very dynamic one—especially in the current day. No one questions the importance of these institutions to our society and culture. *The Board Game* tells a fascinating story about the primary relationship that is crucial for success—the relationship between the CEO (head of school in this case) and the governing board. William Mott has written a book filled with incredible stories of hope and courage. Against a backdrop of institutional rancor, the book's main character comes to terms with his circumstances and seeks ways for others to learn from his experiences. This is a candid and thoughtful look at issues vital to all nonprofit organizations. I highly recommend that both CEOs and governing board members read this book."

Dr. Ted Brown
President of Martin Methodist College (Pulaski, TN)

"At a time when the relationship between trustees and school heads has never been more challenging, William Mott's experience, wisdom, and intelligence act as a beacon through the fog. Dr. Mott's exceptional track record as a successful independent school leader lies at the foundation of *The Board Game* and guides readers through this must-read for all boards of trustees and heads of school. His ability to show the fundamental challenges inherent in the series of complex relationships at the top of all independent schools provides the reader valuable insight into the inner workings of school leadership."

Steven Bristol
Director of Admission, Financial Aid, and Enrollment for
The Hun School of Princeton (Princeton, NJ)

"First of all, *The Board Game* is no game at all. It is a thoughtful, fully experienced collection of relevant issues and strategies in board governance. As an employee and past board member of nonprofit organizations, I can attest to William Mott's approach to solving tough issues for board members in their governance decisions. Dr. Mott's years of experience and range of practical experience, combined with keen insight, give the reader invaluable tools to avoid the pitfalls that so many boards and executives struggle through. Read this book. It just might save your board and your organization!"

Hugh Harris
Headmaster of Franklin Christian Academy (Franklin, TN)

"*The Board Game* is filled with invaluable insights for everyone serving on a corporate board. Guided by his commanding knowledge of board structure and his own personal experiences, William Mott has published an indispensable set of guiding principles that will illuminate the road ahead for board members and organizations alike in developing effective leadership."

Julian Bibb
Community & Nonprofit Leader; Attorney, Stites and Harbison, PLLC

"William Mott's decades of work in the nonprofit sector have given him ample real-world experience working with boards of directors. He has distilled the lessons he's learned and the wisdom he's gained into this readable and accessible book to help everyone who's playing *The Board Game*. It has enhanced my perspective about working with our board of directors and improved our organization as a consequence."

Jeff Wilson
Executive Director, Tennessee Intercollegiate
State Legislature Foundation

"*The Board Game* is highly recommended reading for anyone who attempts to lead an institution, nonprofit, or church board of directors. It traces the life of such a leader whose GPS continually gives the message, 'recalculating route.' With deft precision, William Mott shows us the potholes, detours, road work, and stop signs along the route of working with boards driven by individuals absorbed by power needs, stakeholders with few directions or positive solutions, silent majorities, and a love of the past where the old adage is practiced: 'We've never done it that way before.' Fortunately, his thoughtful insights lead to a conclusion of concrete ways of board leadership development that educates decision makers in how to effectively lead with practicality and wisdom. This is an intelligent approach led by optimism, creativity, and hope from an experienced veteran of 'board games.' I highly endorse Dr. Mott's book as a guide in working with decision-making bodies. It is an excellent resource for anyone who seeks to lead responsibly with clarity and diligence."

The Reverend Doctor Philip W. Leftwich
Executive Presbyter, Honorably Retired,
Presbyterian Church (U.S.A.)

THE
BOARD GAME

A STORY *of*

HOPE *and* INSPIRATION *for*

CEOs and GOVERNING BOARDS

WILLIAM R. MOTT, PH.D.

Editorial—KLOPublishing.com
Typesetting—theDESKonline.com
Cover design—DualIdentityDesign.com

*For Courtney
and our children
Courtney Leigh and Robert*

CONTENTS

PART ONE: JANE

*David comes to terms with his failure to act when the head of
school is threatened. An unexpected turn of events leads David
Andrews to being named interim head of Sanders Academy.*

*As the search process unfolds, David is told about the manner in
which he will be evaluated. David is concerned that it will be an
unachievable standard. Has he been set up to fail?*

*David is named the head of Sanders Academy, but the unortho-
dox behavior on the part of the search committee and the board
of trustees leaves David questioning the process and his future at
the school.*

*David is concerned that the board chair lacks the leadership
and vision needed. He refuses to accept the advice that executive
sessions are not an effective means to build a relationship with
the new head.*

PART TWO: MIKE

PART THREE: CALVIN

FOREWORD BY JACK STANFORD

Nationally Recognized Independent School Leader

A s a child, I remember how difficult it was to play the party game *Pin the Tail on the Donkey,* where one is blindfolded and must successfully aim, without the benefit of sight or direction, and hit the target. Many watched and cheered, but to be successful, one had to navigate by instinct and imagination of one's previous experience with what a donkey looked like with a tail. Defining and pinpointing effective and meaningful leadership roles between the CEO and the board of a nonprofit organization can often be as difficult to achieve as it is to pin the tail on the donkey. William (Bill) R. Mott, Ph.D., has defined these roles and "pinned the tail" in the desired location in his new book.

The Board Game concentrates on the single most important component of successful nonprofit organizations: the relationship between the CEO, the board chair, and the governing board. To be successful, this demands a high level of trust, leadership, collaborative thinking, and extensive cooperation.

Bill's book utilizes fictitious characters to tell his story, but is based on true-life experiences of friends and colleagues he interviewed or has encountered throughout his long career with nonprofit and for-profit organizations. The book is not written as the perfect solution to all conflicts that occur in non-profit organizations. Instead, *The Board Game* is a useful tool for recognizing governance "red flags" that can appear at anytime in a nonprofit organization. Then it suggests how to seek resolutions by applying intelligence and commonsense thinking that is shared equally by the CEO and the board.

An invisible and fragile line exists in nonprofit organizations between the work of the administration and the work of the board. Trouble usually rears its ugly head when either a board member or members cross over that fragile line and begin trying to manage the day-to-day operations of the organization or the CEO crosses that line and begins to make policy for the organization without board approval. Either circumstance can lead to a lack of productivity and a negative direction for the organization. Misfortune usually occurs for the individuals involved and for the organization when that fragile line is destroyed.

Bill is highly qualified to write about that fragile line. He has initiated a successful leadership metamorphous on several occasions between profit and nonprofit organizations. One major reason for his successes is that he remains close to and listens to his constituencies. He has been a top-level administrator in colleges and in independent schools. He founded his own consulting business for assisting schools and colleges with campaigns for growing their annual funds, endowment funds, funds for capital expenditures, and funds for special programs. He has also consulted with numerous nonprofits about their strategic planning and marketing programs.

Presently, there is a subtle transition evolving in the governance of non-profit organizations. I have recognized this transition occurring in several independent schools where I have conducted workshops. Many board members are acting more as managers of committee work and offering less leadership in creative thinking about how to make a good nonprofit organization even better. Managing committee work is necessary and essential for maintaining sustainability and quality, but this work is so time consuming that little or no time is allocated in a board meeting for thinking creatively about the future operations of the organization. On the other side of the table, CEOs are providing more leadership and creative thinking about new ideas, but there is usually insufficient time for the full board to participate in meaningful discussions. The agenda is usually so packed with committee reports that any new ideas are often relegated to a committee. Lost in translation is the corporate thinking of other very intelligent and enthusiastic board members who have a deep affection for the organization and may have the best understanding of how to make the organization more attractive and competitive in the marketplace.

The tail is pinned in all of the wrong places when one works with a blindfold and without the contribution of those around him or her. Time allocated for leadership and managing should be shared equally between the board and the CEO, and sufficient time should be allocated in a board meeting for discussions to ferment. The chair of the board will garner some fruitful insights about leadership and better understand creative thinking about governance after reading *The Board Game.*

I have been privileged to observe Bill in three leadership roles: as a trustee in an independent school; as a candidate for a headship where I served as the search consultant; and as president of an independent school. His calm demeanor, practical reasoning, and thoughtful decision making in these roles ring true in his book.

Bill has written a practical book using work experiences as well as additional case studies to help engage board members and CEOs in meaningful conversations and creative problem solving about governance in nonprofit organizations. I believe any administrator or board member will strive to be a more effective leader after reading *The Board Game.* This book takes off the blindfold and brings participants into the process together in order to make a more meaningful contribution to shared goals.

* * *

Jack Stanford is a nationally recognized independent school leader. He has worked and consulted for over fifty years. Jack has served many schools in a variety of positions including Assistant Head at Baylor School in Chattanooga, Tennessee, Head of School at Presbyterian Day School in Memphis, Tennessee, and President of Hutchison School, also in Memphis. He has served for twenty-six years on the Board of Trustees of several independent schools. In addition he has conducted twenty-three Head of School searches.

Jack has been president of the Southern Association of Independent Schools (SAIS) and the Tennessee Association of Independent Schools (TAIS). In addition Jack chaired the Membership Committee for the National Association of Independent Schools (NAIS). He has received the Distinguished Educational Award for the State of Tennessee and the Sawney Webb Award for outstanding leadership for independent schools also in Tennessee.

INTRODUCTION

"Never underestimate the passion and commitment
of a small group of dedicated individuals to change
the world—indeed it is the only thing that ever has."
—MARGARET MEAD

Anthropologist Margaret Mead's famous approach to changing the world has always been one of my favorite quotes. I suppose I made the assumption that "changing the world" had a positive connotation. Over the past few years, however, I, along with many leaders in the nonprofit world, have come to realize that there also is a negative connotation. Changing the world may not always be a good thing. Specifically, I am referring to the negative influence that governing boards have on the institutions and organizations they are supposed to be serving and supporting.

Almost all nonprofit organizations are structured under the legal and fiduciary responsibility of a governing board. Most state charters and the IRS 501(c)3 designation require that an independent, voluntary board be in place and responsible for the organization. This structure serves schools and nonprofits in a professional manner, demonstrating an understanding and genuine care and concern for what the board believes to be in the organization's best interest. Many boards have an intentional method of operation, but proceed out of unfamiliarity and lack of training. This combination of overconfidence and lack of understanding is hurting many independent schools and organizations, demonstrating limited knowledge of their role, and ultimately hurting the organizations and their leadership.

The Board Game tells the story of David Andrews, president of an independent school. While our hero is a fictional character, his story is a compelling one that could belong to you or many others. The Board Game reflects the concerns and fears of school and nonprofit leaders across the country, exploring numerous ways in which some boards are doing an extremely poor job of carrying out their responsibilities. David's story demonstrates some of the overbearing and misguided behavior that is all too often present. Whether the exception or the rule, what is best for the organization must be the priority. The Board Game is a road map of what to do and what not to do. Although the story is fictional, every Head, Chief Executive Officer (CEO), or Executive Director (ED) and board member will be equipped to identify and recognize the underlying theme and message conveyed in each chapter and each story. All this will lead to strategies for coping with difficult and dysfunctional governing boards and ways in which, over time, these organizations can begin moving forward again.

The research for this book strongly suggests that there needs to be—there *must* be—a partnership that reflects what is best about the relationship between the governing board and the organization's leadership. Recognizing the relationship between the board and leader is critical, what steps are necessary? What lesson can be learned that will make a difference? What seems even more challenging is how this should be accomplished. The board's authority is legally well-defined. Working together to achieve mission, vision, and common goals in a constructive manner is essential. The time has come to help these governing boards by providing solutions to their challenges and recognizing that nonprofit leaders need support rather than coercion to be effective in achieving their mission.

In over twenty-five years in working with schools and non-profit organizations as well as the other organizations I have served as a board member, I have learned that there really are no absolutes. What is very true and troubling for one organization may not in any way relate to another organization. In other words, you may resonate with several issues that are described in this book but not with others.

Another issue to keep in mind is that circumstances can change very quickly. Because your board is functioning at a high level and is both effective and productive, that can change. In a recent conversation with a retired head of school with over twenty years as a school leader, he related the story of a very effective head of school who, when a new board chair took office, was gone in six months. It is this kind of environment that can lead to fear and result in a troubling environment in which to lead a school or nonprofit organization.

Finally, for years I have attended conferences, workshops, and other presentations on the subject of governance of independent schools and nonprofit organizations. Many of these have been worthwhile, effective, and have led to genuine change. Having said that, many of these occasions have included language to suggest, "The board's job is to hire and fire the head (or CEO)." The first one hundred times I heard this I was just numb to what was being said. But over time I began to realize that such words were destructive. Is this the way we really want to convey what the board does—hire and fire? Why not express it this way: "The board's job is to partner with the head (or CEO) in an effort to bring about an exciting mission and vision." That's an organization that I want to be a part of—one that chooses a positive relationship to move forward.

Identifying the issues is a critical first step toward a viable, sustainable relationship. This new model may reveal a new covenant that will lead to a very bright future for schools and all nonprofit organizations. That was my objective when deciding to write this book. My hope is that you will find it to be a useful resource as you lead your school or your nonprofit organization.

PLAYERS IN THE GAME

The Sanders Academy Staff

David Andrews, president of Sanders Academy

Karen Andrews, first lady of Sanders Academy

Sharon Patterson, director of communications

Jim Conrad, academic dean

Dan Reagan, business manager

Ron Hamilton, director of advancement

Warren Hayes, director of development

Mark Martindale, athletic director

Ben Benton, teacher and coach (son of board member Ralph Benton)

Alecia Benton, daughter-in-law of board member Ralph Benton

Scott Holt, head football coach

The Sanders Academy Board

Jane Stevens, first chair of Sanders Academy board of trustees

Mike Riley, second chair

Calvin Dunn, third chair

Tom Foster, former college president

PLAYERS IN THE GAME

Chris Paulson
Randy Lewis, chair of development committee
Anna Watson
Warren Tyler
Ralph Miller
Bart Smith
Mark Davidson
George Alexander
Jackson Lee
Stephanie Roland
Ralph Benton
Jack Montgomery

Other Players

Steve Harding, search consultant
Stan Lealand, former head of Sanders Academy
Robert Mathis

THE
BOARD GAME

"I aspire to inspire before I expire."

—UNKNOWN

"Hope is a good thing, maybe the best of things,
and no good thing ever dies."

—TIM ROBBINS
(As Andy Dufresne in *The Shawshank Redemption*)

PART ONE

JANE

"A prophet is not without honor
except in his hometown ..."
—MARK 6:4

Chapter 1

A WALK IN THE PARK

"Be careful what you wish for . . .
you just might get it."
—UNKNOWN

The November day was cool, but not unexpectedly so for a morning in the South. David Andrews pulled into the parking lot of the city park. His morning walk had become a routine since his doctor told him he needed to lose some weight. The park was beautiful, with over four miles of walking trails. On this particular day, David chose a quarter-mile route. He had walked this oval-shaped section on several other occasions, usually making the loop eight to ten times.

3

David was still upset over the situation with the school where he served as board member as well as chair of the development committee. Over the past few weeks, a handful of board members had orchestrated the removal of the school's head. They argued that she was out of touch. What? She had been an effective leader for a number of years, and the school was thriving in every way. These few trustees took a different view and made their case to a majority of the board. David was busy with his business and simply had not taken the time to confront or discuss the matter with the trustees. He knew something was going on, but little was said openly. As a result, the head's contract was not renewed. She moved on to another leadership role, but it was a sad ending to a stellar career. David was angry with himself for his failure to support her, for not speaking up during the behind-the-scenes discussions about her fate.

What lessons had David learned and what could he do to prevent this from happening again? One fact was clear: a few trustees, who had convinced themselves that this change was essential, had influenced the majority of the board. But was the change necessary? What had been communicated to the head to alert her to any concerns? Were these concerns valid? Had these concerns been shared with the entire board? These were questions that troubled David as he began his walk in the park.

For several months Sanders Academy had been struggling as it conducted a search for a new president—or head of school, as most independent schools called the position. The previous president had retired following a successful fifteen-year tenure. David was in his second year as a board member and had been frustrated by the school's failure to fill the vacancy. So much so that he had entertained thoughts about filling out an application himself. He ultimately decided not to enter the search, though, as he witnessed how brutally the process had been unraveling. *I need to put this behind me,* he thought. *I need to learn from this and do a better job as a trustee.*

About the fifth time around the track, his cell phone rang. David pulled the phone from his pocket and looked to see who was calling him. When he saw the name on the screen, he winced but was not surprised. It was Jane Stevens, the school's chair of the board. David thought, *Now what?* He had endured numerous conversations with Jane over the last few weeks. He had no desire to sacrifice the opportunity to clear his mind and enjoy his quiet morning walk for another dialogue. David shook his head and decided to let her leave a message. He continued his walk, but he couldn't stop wondering why Jane would be calling him at eight on a Monday morning.

David's passion for Sanders Academy was long-term. He had been involved for years, and his father had been a former board chair. Several well-meaning people had tried to convince David to follow in his father's footsteps, but he had been a successful consultant for the past ten years and was reluctant to change course. This independent school, founded in 1911, was well–thought-of in the community and held a special place in David's heart, for he was a graduate, as were his father, brother, and wife.

Jane Stevens had been chair only for a year, but a board

member for almost six years. She was a quiet woman and demonstrated few of the typical leadership qualities needed to run a board consisting of twenty-eight members, five staff members, and three ex-officio members. David considered Jane a somewhat strange choice to be chair. In the months ahead, though, David would discover just how poor a choice Jane truly was.

Following his morning walk, David returned to his office and checked his e-mail. His eyes quickly found one from Sharon Patterson, the school's director of communications, which was directed only to the trustees. David read the message in complete shock. Sanders Academy had called off the search for a new president and was now looking to appoint an interim. To say David was stunned would be an understatement. He wondered, *Is this why Jane was calling me?* Slowly he reached for the phone and punched in Jane's number.

Jane immediately picked up and David apologized for missing her call earlier. As Jane was a woman of few words, she got to the point quickly. She asked David if he would be interested in becoming the interim president of Sanders Academy. David went a little numb. Was this a dream come true or a genuine nightmare? Jane went on to ask if he would come to the school and meet with other trustees. David indicated he would be there in about an hour and then hung up the phone, still in disbelief.

David Andrews, a man in his early forties, was prematurely gray, about 5' 10", and reminded people of a "skinny Philip Seymour Hoffman." He thought Hoffman a good actor but was not sure about the comparison. David's entire career had been in education and consulting. His undergraduate degree in history was from Virginia and his doctorate in education from Texas Christian University.

After the reality of the offer began to set in, David's next thought went to his wife. He and Karen had been married for more than twenty years and shared everything. They met in graduate school and married after he completed his doctorate. She was much smarter and more capable and was devoted to him in ways he did not deserve. He needed her thoughts about this incredible turn of events. He drove directly to her office and told her, "I have been asked to be the interim president at Sanders."

She immediately understood the emotional nature of the news. They embraced, and he provided the details of the conversation. Of his various career moves over the years, this one was the most unexpected and the most exciting.

As a trustee and someone so close to the organization for so long, it never entered David's mind that this opportunity might lead to years filled with verbal abuse, threats, and unrealistic expectations. But that was in the future. Today was all about possibilities and expectations.

Chapter 2

REMOVING "INTERIM" FROM THE TITLE

**"All great deeds and all great thoughts
have a ridiculous beginning."**
—ALBERT CAMUS

After accepting the position, David was determined to conduct the affairs of the school as if he were the president—not merely the interim. He would not behave as any other interim might—serving simply as a caretaker for the organization. The first week was busy, to say the least. The board retreat, scheduled for the first weekend after his appointment, had been on the calendar for many weeks—long before the sudden termination of the search. David was excited about the retreat but nervous about the direction the board would take with the president's position. During the retreat, he began to sense simmering negativity among many board members, as though they resented his appointment.

The result of the retreat was the formation of a commitment to restart the search, with the help of a search consultant and a fourteen-member search committee chaired by Jane Stevens. David knew that it would be a stressful time, but he was determined to work as hard as possible to enhance the work of the school. Fourteen seemed too large a number for a search committee, but he put that thought aside for the moment.

Weeks turned into months, and David made great strides. Excelling in almost every area, Sanders's enrollment and fundraising were breaking records, and morale among faculty and staff was high. Parents' concerns were being heard and the atmosphere was positive. Little was said about the search, and David focused on his work. After about five months, the search process had settled on three finalists, including David. Everyone at the school could see that he was doing an excellent job. He had embraced his work with passion and enthusiasm, and much had been accomplished during his short time there.

> After about five months, the search process had settled on three finalists, including David.

The other two finalists each spent two days on campus meeting with the search committee, faculty, staff members, and others close to the school. David did his best to make himself scarce while the candidates were around. As it turned out, David was the last of the three candidates to be interviewed. Because of his knowledge of the school, his status as a former board member, his role as interim president, and his commitment to Sanders, he approached the two-day interview with confidence and enthusiasm.

When the interview process concluded around six o'clock p.m. that Wednesday, David truly believed he had tried his best and done well. The search consultant asked David to wait in his office. Karen had sat in on several of the interview sessions and had seen her husband in a completely new light. She remarked to a friend, "I was really impressed by how articulate and knowledgeable David was. I sort of saw him as just the guy who took out the trash."

A little after eight o'clock p.m., the search consultant, Steve Harding, came in to present the news to a very nervous interim president. David had known and been very friendly with Steve for several years. He was a very experienced consultant and had worked on the search since the very beginning.

Steve entered David's office with a big smile. He wasted no time. "David, the search committee has selected you as the new president. Congratulations!" These words meant more than almost any David had ever heard. He went a little numb. Steve continued, "The search committee wants to create a unique way to evaluate your performance. I don't know all of the details, but I believe it will have several criteria—including the goal of raising one million dollars every year for the annual fund and increasing enrollment by 5 percent a year. Quite honestly, I think it is very odd, but they will explain it to you."

David blinked at this. Although he knew from the interview that the search committee felt it was important to make a bold statement regarding raising funds and addressing the declining enrollment, he did not realize it was going to be a formal component of the evaluation process. His mind also began to calculate the implications of the annual fund goal, which was just $350,000 the previous year. The last two days had been life-changing, and he needed time to absorb it all.

One of the finalists had been a charismatic leader from the corporate world. Clearly, this was a departure from the more traditional model of an individual with significant experience in the school or nonprofit world. His message to the search committee was, "Yes, I can—whatever you need, I can achieve on a faster timetable than you think possible." Of course, the search committee was enthralled with such promises. When asked whether it was possible to raise one million dollars the following year and increase enrollment by 5 percent, this candidate responded, "Yes, it is possible, and I could raise that amount each year and accomplish your enrollment objectives!" A completely blind promise based on no experience in raising money or enrolling students for any school. Regardless, the damage was done—this new standard was now in the minds of the search committee and would help them determine whether or not the next president was successful. There was no way for David to predict what a nightmare this would become.

Chapter 3

THE BEGINNING
OF THE END

"Anyone who has never made a mistake
has never tried anything new."
—ALBERT EINSTEIN

Although David was very excited about the opportunity to serve as president and make a difference, he was concerned about the way in which the board had handled this entire matter. In reflection, he could see why the earlier search had failed to yield a candidate—the process had been flawed by the behavior of many of the board members. Now he felt he was going down the wrong path in his relationship with the board. A troubling pattern was emerging.

David was confident that the called board meeting to hear the recommendation of the search committee would be quick; he assumed the board would enthusiastically ratify the recommendation of the search committee.

This turned out to not be the case.

David remained in his office awaiting the outcome. Thirty minutes turned into an hour, and then an hour and a half. By now, David was convinced something had gone terribly wrong. Finally at 6:45, the board members emerged—but no one came by to tell him any news. Outside his office, he could see their smiling, confident, happy expressions as they left. What had happened?

As it turned out, there was a special event scheduled that evening honoring the faculty. David was aware of the event but had not been told there was going to be an announcement. The board chair assumed David would be there and would use this opportunity to make the announcement. David's wife realized what had taken place and immediately called him at his office. He raced over to the party to be a part of the announcement that the board had selected him as the new president. The faculty and staff enthusiastically applauded the announcement. It would be several years before he was told the truth about what actually occurred at the board meeting that night. It truly was the beginning of the end.

David understood that leadership is critical in the success or failure of an organization.

> David's greatest fear was that the school's board was not fully committed to his leadership.

Passion, vision, commitment, and the ability to make difficult decisions embody the qualities of a great leader, but when there is a leadership vacancy, especially in a governing body, staff morale will suffer and the organization will falter. David's greatest fear was that the school's board was not fully committed to his leadership. Why would they have imposed an assessment tool that would make it nearly impossible to succeed? Even though David had an amazing track record in raising money, he knew that failure was almost assured within the current structure.

Later, David and Jane discussed how he would be able to overcome a deficiency in one area by having greater success in others, but this understanding was not clearly communicated to either the executive committee or the full board. They would be far less flexible, and it quickly became apparent that there was more than one agenda in play. Ultimately, a leadership failure would cripple the school and result in a host of changes.

Chapter 4

THE EXECUTIVE SESSION SAGA

"An army of lions commanded by a deer
will never be an army of lions."
—NAPOLEON

David had always been an active volunteer, serving on numerous boards of trustees and directors. Not only was it the right thing to do, but he also recognized it as beneficial to the entire management process of a nonprofit organization. As a board member, he was familiar with executive sessions. Such sessions typically followed the regular board meeting and excluded all members of the staff—usually including the CEO of the organization.

But why? What purpose did they serve? David thought such

sessions pointlessly demonstrated a lack of support for the CEO. As a board member of other organizations, executive sessions usually were prompted only by the necessity of discussing compensation for the CEO.

This was about to change dramatically. Following his first board meeting as president of Sanders Academy, the chair unexpectedly requested that everyone on the staff be excused—except for David and the academic dean, Jim Conrad. David was surprised, to say the least, that he had not been told about this session. The chair then asked each member if they had questions or concerns about anything. It quickly turned into a gripe session in which board members took aim at whatever topic they believed needed addressing. Occasionally, David looked over at the chair as she allowed these mini-tirades to continue.

Nothing. No reaction of any kind. After about twenty-five minutes, the chair requested that David and Jim leave the room. Again, David expressed surprise that the board would meet without him, giving him no indication as to their agenda.

David was sure the chair would call him the next morning to share what had taken place the night before. But no call ever came. David was left to speculate about what had been discussed and what decisions had been made. Where was the support from the chair? David desperately wanted to be included, to be a partner in the process, but this was not to be.

The idea of the executive sessions was troubling. The reality was much worse, though. What the trustees were saying during the time David was allowed to be present had almost nothing to do with governance but rather a range of complaints—issues that should have been addressed outside of this meeting on an individual basis. They were mostly operational matters that had no place in an executive session, let alone a board meeting. Furthermore, several board members challenged the academic dean in a manner that was barely civil. Jim Conrad was an excellent dean, who did not even report to the board. David wanted to remind these board members that he, David, was their only employee. If they had issues with the dean's performance, then such concerns should be addressed to the president. Their attitude and actions were terrible enough, but it was even worse that this offensive behavior seemed to be encouraged.

A few days following the meeting, David had a conversation with a new trustee he thought he could trust.

"You mean Jane didn't call you?" Tom Foster said in dismay.

David replied, "I have not heard a word."

Tom seemed very surprised by this. However, still nothing happened. David knew he should request a meeting to find out what the chair's intentions were, but after several days he decided to let the matter drop and braced himself for what the trustees would do next.

At the next board meeting, it became apparent that the executive sessions would be the new way of doing business. David reflected sadly on what could have been. The executive session again allowed the trustees to sound off on issues that did not concern them. Again, many inappropriate remarks were made at the expense of the academic dean. Also, as in the previous meeting, both the president and the dean were dismissed with no follow-up communication.

David was not sure where to turn. Tom Foster, the new trustee, was a retired college president who had a long career working successfully with governing boards. He would reach out to Tom for advice and counsel. Tom had not yet attended a board meeting, and David was certain he could demonstrate what a bad idea these executive sessions were. When they met, David explained what had been occurring at the board meetings. Tom said all the right things. He expressed alarm at the actions of the board. Then David asked, "What can we do—actually, what can *you* do to help?" David was well aware that only someone of Tom's stature would have any influence over the board chair. He left their meeting hopeful.

> These sessions clearly demonstrated to David that he and the board were not working as one to advance the school and its mission.

David was well aware that resource literature on the subject said executive sessions were a necessary part of governance, especially when evaluating and compensating an organization's president or CEO, but this practice at Sanders Academy was destructive. These sessions clearly demonstrated to David that he and the board were not working as one to advance the school and its mission. It was so obvious. Why didn't the board, or at least the board chair, see this?

A few months prior, all of the new board members had participated in an orientation session designed to better acquaint themselves with the college, as well as to learn principles of good practice for being a beneficial board member. The orientation facilitator had told them that executive sessions were non-productive and usually resulted in little that was useful and much that was toxic regarding the relationship between the board and CEO. And yet here they were, ignoring the advice of a recognized expert and behaving in a way that exposed their lack of support for the president. David was really counting on Tom.

A few days later, Tom had an opportunity to meet with board chair Jane Stevens. Tom explained his concern regarding the executive sessions, pointing out that these meetings gave the very strong impression that the board was not fully supportive of President Andrews and Academic Dean Conrad. After Tom's thoughtful explanation, based on years of experience, he waited for Jane to respond.

Jane simply said, "Tom, I thank you for expressing your opinion on this matter; but I have spoken with other trustees, and they feel strongly that they need to have an opportunity to express their opinions and concerns. Andrews and Conrad need to get used to this, because it will continue."

Tom was stung by this response and added, "Jane, I disagree with this practice, but you are the chair and I respect your authority to conduct meetings in a way you feel is important." Then he added, "I would, however, encourage you to communicate with David what topics are discussed in the sessions after he and Jim Conrad are dismissed."

Jane promised that she would communicate with David following each board meeting, but the executive sessions continued in the same way and with nothing communicated to David afterward. Tom knew this was wrong. Why had he not done more to support the president on this critical issue? Later, David suggested to Tom that this be a topic discussed during the board meeting in an effort to see how the board really felt, but Tom felt the chair would not allow this to become an agenda item.

David knew this was an issue that was holding back the board in its effectiveness. If they could be sidetracked by executive sessions, then they were missing genuine opportunities to partner with the president and academic dean to explore important topics that could lead to meaningful change. David knew the school was suffering from the board's self-serving, negative behavior. He also knew he was trapped, having to work with a chair who was unwilling to change and a board member who knew better but was not in a powerful enough position to bring about change. David felt his only course was to make the best of a bad situation.

David had served on numerous boards and had never before felt the inclination to be so bold as to disrupt the entire board. As he reflected on what he had to deal with—knowing that it was damaging the school—it was a clear reminder of the importance of attitude and how it so profoundly impacts you and those around you. He was reminded of the Thomas Jefferson quote, "Nothing can stop someone with the right attitude, and nothing on earth can help someone with a poor attitude." All the skills and knowledge in the world were of little use when forced to work with someone who had a negative and destructive attitude. He would reflect on this many times over the next several years, and he would do all he could to ensure that people with a positive, supportive attitude be sought for membership on the board. He knew that of all the characteristics needed by a board member, this one must rise to the top and become a strategic priority.

Chapter 5

INDECENT
PROPOSALS

"The challenge of leadership is to be strong, but not rude;
be kind, but not weak; be bold, but not bully;
be thoughtful, but not lazy; be humble, but not timid;
be proud, but not arrogant; have humor, but without folly."
—JIM ROHN

There is no better place to be during the fall than on a school campus. The beauty of the grounds, the activities of students, and the general sense of excitement all reveal that being a part of a school community is very special. David Andrews believed this and always felt blessed to have an opportunity to make a difference in the lives of students. He loved leading the school, working with faculty and staff, reaching out to alumni, and finding ways to advance the school. In fact, David loved everything about his career, save one—his continuing, and growing, problem with the board. It seemed that everything he was trying to do was being undermined by the board—or at least certain members. In spite of so many factors, the board viewed the school's progress with more and more skepticism. These few trustees often questioned David's leadership.

In the late fall a student had been caught cheating—a violation of the school's well-known honor code. Always a troubling situation, this one was more difficult because it involved a highly regarded student who had an impeccable record. The situation was well reviewed by both President Andrews and Dean Conrad, who agreed on the consequences by adhering to guidelines found in the student handbook as well as conducting interviews with all parties involved. Although this was a very painful and discouraging situation, both David and Jim felt the decision made was the correct response. Not everyone agreed, though. The family of the student was outraged and filed a lawsuit, something the school anticipated since it was all too familiar with lawsuits.

This event had everyone on edge and was all anyone was talking about. It was clearly an unpopular decision but one that had to be made. The mood around campus for several days was poor. How could this happen to such a model student? The president and the dean were pressured to reverse their decision. Some people felt strongly that the student had not been cheating but rather taking advantage of information available on the Web. The teacher believed her instructions were clear regarding not using the Internet. Back and forth the discussions went.

Eventually the lawsuit would go to mediation for a resolution, with the academic dean representing the school. After almost six hours of mediation, the decision was made to uphold the school's position given the nature of the infraction. Both David and Jim hoped this would end the debate, but that was not the case.

No sooner had the case been resolved than Chris Paulson, a trustee, suggested that the school had been wrong and the student should suffer no consequences for his actions. The CEO of a large accounting firm, Paulson's daughter had graduated from Sanders several years earlier. He was well-educated and considered himself an expert on most any topic. Furthermore, he was very wealthy and never passed on an opportunity to remind people of his power and influence. Early in his tenure, David tried to develop a relationship with Chris. They had known each other as fellow board members before David was appointed president. However, it did not take long for David to feel bullied and threatened by Chris. He had told the board chair of his concerns, but nothing was done about it.

Paulson did everything possible to overturn the decision the two chief officers had made, eventually sending a proposal to Jane Stevens, the board chair, demanding that the decision be reversed and that no penalties be imposed on the student. The correct response would have been for the chair to inform Chris that his actions were in direct violation of his responsibilities as a trustee and that he must withdraw his proposal. Best practice clearly states that trustees should not be advocating for families in opposition to the school's administrative leadership.

Further, he should have been told that if he persisted he would have to step down from the board. There was no discipline exhibited by the chair or the executive committee when it came to the behavior of board members, though. It was the wild west with no sheriff in town!

At the next executive committee meeting, the chair brought the proposal up for the committee to consider. David was astounded but kept silent. Apparently other board members were equally shocked that the chair would allow this to be discussed. One of the members, Ralph Miller, did not mince words: "I am outraged that Chris would bring this before the executive committee. The administration has worked hard to resolve this matter. Further, disciplinary actions and violations of the honor code are not our responsibility. This matter should be considered closed."

The other committee members had never seen Ralph quite so agitated. Ralph was a solid board member and could always be counted on for his objective and thoughtful views on all issues concerning the school. He recommended that the chair communicate to Paulson that the matter was closed and that he should step down if he persisted.

This whole affair caused David to reflect on another aspect of this incident: parents going to board members to resolve their issues was a growing concern. Much of the blame for this trend rested on the board—either they didn't know it was inappropriate or they were abusing their position of power and influence. He knew it would be difficult to alter the views and actions of parents, but the board was another matter. He made a note to address the matter at the next orientation session.

> This whole affair caused David to reflect on another aspect of this incident: Parents going to board members to resolve their issues was a growing concern.

David's mind returned to the specific matter at hand, and he was pleasantly surprised by the turn of events, thanks to Ralph Miller. Was it possible that this would be Chris Paulson's last attack on the administration? Regrettably, another episode was just around the corner, this one concerning a member of the college faculty and in an operational area that had little to do with the board of trustees. That, of course, made no difference to Paulson.

A member of the faculty had participated in a highly questionable activity in his classroom. Recognizing the importance of academic freedom, administrators had warned this teacher against something they considered indefensible. For the most part this teacher was well-thought-of and popular with many students, but his recent conduct was beyond questionable. David knew there was a genuine possibility of a lawsuit based on sexual harassment, so he and the dean discussed how best to resolve the matter. They began, as usual, with the students' best interests in mind while also considering the impact a decision may have on the faculty member as well as the institution. Personnel matters such as this one were filled with emotion and drama, with no easy solution.

Following an extensive investigation and review it was decided that this faculty member's contract would not be renewed. He would, however, be compensated with salary and benefits for a period of six months in recognition of his contributions to the school during his many years of service. Both David and Jim, along with business manager Dan Reagan, held this to be the best possible decision given the circumstances. Not surprisingly, the teacher disagreed with the decision, feeling strongly that the situation had been blown way out of proportion when an offended student went to her parents. The parents made it clear that the school needed to take action by sending a tough message that such conduct would not be tolerated. Soon, however, things began to get very interesting, and the well-intentioned plans began to unravel when Chris Paulson unethically and inappropriately interjected himself into the situation. Upon hearing the decision of the administration he unilaterally decided that the faculty member had not been treated fairly. Without consulting with the administration or the board, Chris reached out to the faculty member to see how he might intervene on his behalf.

On a Sunday afternoon, David received a call from another parent informing him that he had been contacted by Paulson on behalf of the teacher and was now trying to mediate the situation. David, having been friends with this parent for a number of years, tried to subtly explain that the final decision had been made with no further discussion necessary. The parent, though, made it equally clear that this response was unacceptable and that the teacher was planning to sue the school for wrongful termination and age discrimination.

Over the next several weeks the phone call led to many more phone calls, meetings, and discussions. Because of the harmful intrusion by a trustee, what was already a difficult and emotional situation became almost unbearable. David, Jim, and Dan Reagan worked hard to resolve the matter—again. In the end, the administration was forced to modify the agreement with the dismissed faculty member.

Years later when David reflected on this ugly episode, he wondered what could have been done differently. How do schools keep from appointing board members who power-up and threaten others? The only way to deal with a bully is to confront them and address unacceptable behavior head-on. One thing was clear: organizations must do a better job of screening prospective board members. The other point of clarity was that leadership always makes a difference. The presence of strong, effective leadership will triumph and in the end, will be enormously beneficial for the organization. Unfortunately, that kind of leadership was absent and there was little David could do. A handful of individuals had taken over and he knew only the most radical of changes would have any impact.

Chapter 6

THOSE WHO NEVER GET IT

"All cruel people describe themselves
as paragons of frankness."
—TENNESSEE WILLIAMS

D an Reagan had been the business manager for many years,
but he was not exactly the stereotypical accountant type.
He first became acquainted with the school when his children
attended and then graduated from Sanders. A complex individual, he could be gregarious, funny, interesting . . . and slightly
annoying, especially when he went on and on about the Yellow
Jackets of his alma mater, Georgia Tech. However, he understood
people and was an astute judge of character. He and President

Andrews had known each other for years and were friends as well as colleagues. They were different in many ways, but one thing they certainly had in common was a belief in Sanders Academy and its future.

As David considered his perilous position with the board, he remembered one of Dan's favorite expressions: "They all get it 95 percent of the time." What he was referring to was his belief that the trustees understood their role and responsibilities 95 percent of the time. The trustees seemed to have amnesia the other 5 percent. While David believed this to be true for most board members, there were some for whom those figures were reversed. Regardless of the situation or circumstances, these trustees reacted 95 percent of the time by meddling in matters that did not concern them, interceding when it was dishonorable, and making subtle yet definite threats against the administration. If confronted they would, of course, react with shock and dismay, denying any misconduct on their part. If questioned about their intentions (which almost *never* happened), they asserted that they had been misunderstood. Most often, though, they operated under the pretext that as trustees it was their right to intervene whenever and wherever they chose.

At Sanders Academy, three of these board members stood out to David as the worst of the worst: Anna Watson, Bart Smith, and Mark Davidson. Later, David concluded that these three had been the architects of the plan meant to damage his career at Sanders Academy. While David was not a psychologist, he couldn't help trying to determine why their

David concluded that these three had been the architects of the plan meant to damage his career at Sanders Academy.

attitudes and actions were often so offensive, so negative, so counterproductive. David knew from his experience on other boards
that these three represented something of an oddity. Nonetheless,
birds of a feather flock together, and so it seemed that they had
teamed up to make sure he failed. These three were on the search
committee, and they all voted for the other finalist. Of course it
was their prerogative to vote for the other candidate. However,
they should not have remained on the board if they were unable
to support the candidate selected by the full board.

These three board members, plus others at times, were at
odds with David and others in the administration. There were no
celebrations for accomplishments, and criticisms flowed freely.
This negative behavior caused David to be paranoid, and for good
reason. It was bad enough how he was regarded in public that
he could imagine what negative things were said in the private,
unsanctioned meetings, which encouraged distrust and antago-
nism among the board and administration.

Anna Watson had a most unflattering nickname that reflected
the current vampire craze and was an obvious nod to her personality. There was no issue on which Anna wasn't an expert. David
was well aware of her reputation to be extremely critical in usually
uncivil and divisive ways. She was one of the most negative people David had ever met. At board meetings she questioned almost
everything and essentially waged war on anything the administration did or proposed. It was evident that she enjoyed the sound
of her own voice, which she used to intimidate, bully, threaten,
and meddle as she addressed matters that should have never been
discussed by the board. She claimed to be a respected leader in
the community, but David found that most people avoided her or

simply did not take her seriously. How had she gotten into such a position of leadership on the board?

Bart Smith was a man of many accomplishments—and he made sure people knew about each and every one of them. He found fault with many things, including liberal arts colleges, which he called "an impractical waste of time." He would say to David that this administrator or that faculty member should be fired. Why? Because Bart thought he was all-knowing and had the right to say who comes and who goes. He made it onto the board because he had made a donation to the school and, therefore, someone thought he should be thanked with a seat on the board. Unfortunately, a generous giver is not always an asset as a board member. Ironically, not only had Anna Watson rarely made a gift, several times she had failed to fulfill her pledge. Yet there she was on the board—the biggest talker but smallest giver.

Mark Davidson had raised the faithful questions to each candidate, "Can you raise one million dollars every year for the annual fund?" and "Can you increase enrollment by 5 percent each year?" Of course, he had no idea what this meant or what would be involved in raising that kind of money. Sanders Academy had a somewhat sketchy history when it came to raising money. The figure thrown out was arbitrary and not tied to any program, project, or initiative. Mark didn't understand the needs of the school, but as an educated man, he thought he knew all he needed to know about education. He was a lawyer who could exude charm out one side of his mouth while talking down to you out the other.

Mark participated in numerous secret board meetings in which he portrayed David as a failure and unworthy of being president. Because of this, certain trustees made pronouncements about specific matters without seeing the whole picture. Mark continuously refused to recognize genuine accomplishments by David that were clearly advancing the institution. Nothing David did was enough for Mark, who only cared about hitting the magic one million dollar mark instead of focusing on what was critical to the school's future, such as enrollment, retention, and growing capital and endowment funds. And since David had not achieved what Mark wanted, David had to go!

David tried but couldn't put it out of his mind that these three trustees had favored the other candidate, a viable choice who offered unique strengths and strategies as a result of his corporate leadership experience. What kept coming back to David, though, was Steve Harding, the search consultant. What was his reaction to this situation? What did he say to the trustees the night of the search committee vote? Did he indicate to the search committee the importance of consensus even if the initial vote was not unanimous? How the search process unfolded would have much to do with the way in which David Andrews would be treated.

There was no doubt in David's mind that Steve Harding had done a completely professional search and had done his best to ensure that once a decision was made, the entire search committee would confirm the decision of the majority. What Steve had no control over was the way in which all of this played out over time. The full board demonstrated behavior that made it clear there was division. While they may have verbally committed to David, their actions reflected a very different reality.

One of the aspects that made David unique as president is that almost everyone saw him from a very different perspective. To many he was an alumnus. To others he was a parent. And to a few he was a trustee. Almost nobody knew him exclusively as the president of the school. David saw his various relationships to the school as an incredible advantage. Someone with so close an association with the school would have an understanding and affection few others would possess. If this were the case, why were these trustees so determined that he should fail? He often thought about this and believed there truly must be something to the biblical expression, "A prophet is not without honor except in his hometown." David knew that regardless of what was accomplished, his days were numbered.

Chapter 7

THE LONE RANGERS

"I've learned that people will forget what you said,
people will forget what you did, but people will
never forget how you made them feel."
—MAYA ANGELOU

Although David served as president of the school, he had been a member of several nonprofit boards, including some independent school boards. He reflected that never had he witnessed the kind of behavior exhibited by the board and the board leadership of Sanders Academy. Why was that? Why was this board so dysfunctional, so disrespectful, so unwilling to recognize legitimate accomplishments of the school? David had been around leaders for much of his career and believed he recognized the difference between effective leaders and those who were out of their element. The chair of the Sanders Academy board fit the latter description.

One of the principle characteristics needed of a board chair is the willingness and resolve to discipline any trustee who behaves in a manner that is harmful to the organization, and David was absolutely sure there were several trustees who needed a review of their actions. In discussing this issue with other nonprofit leaders, David discovered that this issue was almost universally ignored by chairs since no one enjoys confronting a board peer. At some institutions, situations are exacerbated when the board chair is related to, or doing business with, another trustee. David viewed such circumstances as a conflict of interest—and putting the interests of certain individuals above those of the organization was completely wrong. Yet, there it was—an environment that was difficult because of board members being related to or working with one another. And David could do nothing that could effectively address this situation.

Conflict of interest represents a very important ethical matter for any board to be aware of because, given such a situation, it's very difficult—if not impossible—to discern whether people's actions are for the best interest of the organization or the individuals involved. David believed there are certain universal truths when it came to this matter, and so he developed a list of warning signs to help him

> David developed a list of warning signs to help him recognize when someone was putting self or another chosen individual's interests above the organization.

recognize when someone was putting self or another chosen individual's interests above the organization:

1. Trustees who allow the business they do together outside of the boardroom to influence the decisions they make inside of it.

2. Trustees who allow issues that are not appropriate to discuss in the boardroom, using the venue to perpetuate their agenda.

3. Trustees who demand their way on a range of issues and threaten to withhold support if their "demands" are not met.

4. Trustees who use their position on the board to obtain business opportunities or recognition without concern as to how it may impact the board and organization.

5. Trustees who meet in secret and maintain that such actions are part of what is necessary, claiming such unsanctioned meetings are appropriate.

6. Trustees who bully the organization's leadership without regard to the professional and personal damage it causes.

What upset David most was that he knew there was likely no amount of professional board workshops, training, retreats, etc., that would ever eliminate this type of behavior altogether. Therefore, he was fully convinced that only through board members' positive attitudes, principles, and values would a board become a positive catalyst for change. David thought, *If you invite a bully to be on your board, then don't be surprised when you are bullied.*

Chapter 8

DRESSED TO KILL

"Power tends to corrupt and
absolute power corrupts absolutely."
—Lord Acton

As a trustee for several years before becoming president of the school, David had been involved in the decision regarding uniforms for students. While a very controversial topic at many independent and charter schools, at Sanders it had been a relatively painless process. In the decade since the decision had been made, there had been few modifications to the uniforms. When David was named president, one of the items on his to-do list was another modification based on his much larger campus-wide branding initiative.

An ad hoc committee was established to address this particular issue and make a recommendation to the board of trustees for their "approval." Technically, such an issue would not come under the purview of the board as it was an operational and administrative matter, but David wanted their input. The board voted unanimously in support of the change that both David and the committee had proposed.

In the spring semester, David began making plans for the uniform change to go into effect when the new academic year began in August. They decided to contract with a well-known catalog company that provided school uniforms as a part of their service. Everything was going smoothly—apparently too smoothly.

As a part of David's desire to adequately communicate the change, e-mails were sent and information was posted on the school's Web site as well. Then the trouble began. An alumnus, who had been opposed to uniforms in the first place, was convinced this most recent change was too much. She started speaking out against the change and eventually got the ear of a member of the board of trustees.

David knew that the manner in which effective, partnering boards worked best was for the board member in such a situation to thank the individual for her concern and suggest that she contact the school president, who would be able to explain the thoroughness of the process.

> David's authority was being undermined by a board member who obviously did not understand the proper role of a trustee in this situation.

As is all too often the case, to the contrary, the board member offered to intervene on her behalf and bring the matter directly to the executive committee for discussion.

The board member contacted David to inform him he had communicated with the board chair and that an executive committee meeting was called for the next week, whereby David could defend his decision regarding the variation to the uniform. David indicated to the executive committee that he could meet, but he was stunned by this complete lack of protocol. He told them that the new uniform was approved and the school's order had already been placed in anticipation of a July delivery date.

David's authority was being undermined by a board member who obviously did not understand the proper role of a trustee in this situation, but without the support of the board chair in this matter, there was little to do but attend the meeting. It was another example of a trustee who attended an orientation session—one in which such issues were discussed—but either did not listen, did not care, or couldn't say no to an alumnus. This situation was practically identical to some of the case studies discussed. Why didn't board members realize that such actions did not represent best practices? *Effective boards understand the difference*, thought David, *or perhaps they just listen better at orientation sessions.*

On the day of the executive committee meeting, David had a family medical emergency that took him away from campus. He e-mailed the board chair to inform her of his inability to attend the meeting, fully expecting that it would be rescheduled. Later that day, though, David was shocked to receive an e-mail from the chair stating that the meeting would indeed be held as originally scheduled!

The executive committee met and discussed the objection by the alumnus over the uniform change—the very same change that the board had already approved. In a demonstration that conveyed a complete lack of support for David as well as a disregard for their role, the executive committee recommended the matter be taken back to the full board for resolution. Their actions also spoke volumes as to how they viewed and valued the relationship between the head and the board.

This matter would have never seen the light of day if only the trustee had told the alumnus that the uniform change had been researched, reviewed, and communicated to everyone impacted by the change. Instead, hours were spent on a matter that David had appropriately and conclusively resolved—and acted upon when he placed the order with the supplier.

David had no alternative other than to present his case to the trustees—much as he had done at the earlier board meeting. The ensuing discussion was combative as members of the executive committee argued not to adopt the uniform change while other trustees, resentful of the high-handed tactics of the executive committee, spoke in support of David and the logical, thoughtful way in which he presented his case for the change.

In the end, a compromise was struck. The trustees delayed any change to the uniform for one year, at which time the matter could again be brought before the board for consideration.

Many questions ran through David's head:

- *What were the lessons learned from this experience?*

- *What could I have done differently to produce a different outcome?*

- *How does one deal with a small number of vocal individuals who want their way regardless of process or who it affects?*

Convinced that this situation further undermined his relationship with the board, David continued to wonder when—or if—genuine leadership would ever be exhibited by this board. He was on the road to perdition, and there was no exit.

Chapter 9

A LEGACY CHALLENGED

"They're more like guidelines..."
—*Geoffrey Rush*
(as Barbossa in *Pirates of the Caribbean*)

W ith every board the issues surrounding tenure (length of service), board terms, rotation, etc., are discussed often and, more times than not, are somewhat controversial. David was well aware that the prevailing wisdom on the subject leaned heavily on having specified board terms, which are sometimes referred to as "term limits" (particularly when thinking of political offices).

At Sanders Academy these issues had been discussed from

time to time, but with no sense of urgency to change much of anything. The Sanders bylaws had fixed terms, but no term limits. In other words, trustees were asked to serve a three-year term. In theory a trustee could be reelected to an endless number of three-year terms, although the norm in the nonprofit world was that a trustee only serves two successive three-year terms. Afterward, the trustee must step down from the board for at least one year. Certainly there were numerous exceptions to this, but more and more organizations were adopting this. The fundamental reason behind this was to ensure a continuing turnover that would infuse new ideas, new strengths, and new approaches to the board's work. Having three-year terms also provided a process by which trustees who were not performing as expected could be removed from their service. Far too few organizations take advantage of this opportunity to rid themselves of trustees who don't offer anything constructive or helpful to the organization. What tends to happen is that even the worst board members linger on and on, taking the space and place of someone who would be a productive member of the board.

Because of the way in which the bylaws were written, several Sanders board members had enjoyed being on the board for many years

> Several Sanders board members had enjoyed being on the board for many years (in some cases, decades) yet offered little value to their position.

(in some cases, decades) yet offered little value to their position. In some instances, members were very detrimental to the school, using their position, and perhaps longevity, as an opportunity to oppose innovation, creativity, and most any idea put forward by David. One such trustee was Jack Montgomery.

Jack had been a trustee for more than twenty years. He was an alumnus of the school, but he also had inherited significant money and was something of a local celebrity. He was the kind of person who did everything possible to enhance his wealth—often at the expense of others. To some he had a reputation for being a southern gentleman who was polite and gentile. To many others, though, he was seen as a ruthless businessman. He had an appearance that reminded many people of Charles Dickens's character Scrooge; he was small, thin, slightly stooped, and an unpleasant scowl was almost always part of his demeanor. Truly, though, he was a combination of those two extreme personalities.

David did not like, trust, or respect Jack, mostly because he just took up space at the board table. His giving was significantly below his capacity, he believed David and the senior administrators existed only to serve his needs, and he had business ties with several trustees, which David thought was a conflict of interest.

Jack Montgomery had not made an annual fund gift in three years, even though he had made a significant pledge to the capital campaign several years ago. Despite the efforts of many, no one had been able to get one dime from him. There were occasional vague promises of a payment, accompanied by numerous excuses as to why nothing had happened.

This predicament finally came to a head when the school's independent auditors questioned the pledge and its status. It was the moment of truth. Finally, there would be some resolution. He would have to commit or be forced to admit that he did not intend to fulfill his obligation.

No one wanted to confront Jack on the issue. The fact that the school would reach this point with a trustee was unfathomable to David. Why would someone who was clearly capable of honoring a generous pledge consciously decide not to do so? Why would someone under these circumstances be allowed to remain on the board? Why did the chair of the board not challenge Jack? Was Jack so oblivious that he did not recognize the damage he was doing by his inaction?

David knew the answer. Jack was the type of person to whom this cliché applied: "Seldom wrong, never in doubt." He possessed a level of arrogance David rarely witnessed in people. It was almost as if the rules did not apply to Jack Montgomery.

In schools and organizations that have language in their bylaws regarding board term limits, this could have been addressed and taken care of a long time ago. David was convinced that even had the verbiage been found in the bylaws, it most likely would have been ignored since leadership on the whole saw bylaws as simply guidelines or even suggestions—especially when it came to an issue the board preferred to ignore.

David wanted to challenge this idea. He wanted Jack to be held accountable for what he was doing—or not doing. He was tired of seeing Jack get a free pass for many of his transgressions. But, of course, nothing was going to happen. Board chair Jane Stevens would take no action against this trustee icon. Oh, maybe she would have a conversation with Jack, but in no way would she hold him accountable. In reality how could she? The two worked together on numerous business ventures. David knew that in the best case scenario, the chair would go only so far and then abandon the idea that Jack was responsible for his disregard of his financial commitment to the school. It would be business as usual. David knew that the bylaws needed to be changed. But he recognized that any new bylaws would be seen only as guidelines. Only the infusion of new and different thinking would cause such changes to become a reality.

Chapter 10

NATURAL SELECTION

"If we are together nothing is impossible,
if we are divided all will fail."
—SIR WINSTON CHURCHILL

A lthough David's relationship with the trustee leadership
was seldom what he hoped it would be, he always was
aware that new trustees, with new perspectives, could change
the dynamic of the organization. The Committee on Trustees
rarely sought David's input when it came time to reach out to
prospective trustees. David provided input to the committee as
to whom he thought would be a "good trustee," which could be
defined in so many ways. Did a good trustee have great instincts,
act on hunches, offer valuable input, make decisions based on

data, or all of the above? David believed that much had to do with observation.

Over the past few years, David became more and more convinced that observation, actions, and communication were as important as anything else when it came to selecting effective trustees. David had observed the behavior, demeanor, and attitude of several individuals he thought would be good candidates. When it came time to meet with the committee, he made a number of recommendations and was surprised that the committee was going to actually act on some of his recommendations. What amazed David during his time at Sanders, though, was that he was never included on visits to invite new trustees to join the board. Here he was the CEO of the organization, but it was shocking to see the lack of trust and support that existed between David and the board.

> What amazed David was that he was never included on visits to invite new trustees to join the board.

One prospective trustee was Jackson Lee. Over the previous two years, David had gotten to know Jackson very well. A successful business owner, Jackson was very bright, funny, articulate, and supportive of the school and its leadership. He grew up in Charlotte, North Carolina, and was the product of an excellent independent school. Although not overly generous, Jackson had many qualities David was seeking in a trustee. He also appeared to be unafraid of the executive committee and not susceptible to other members' tactics. David was pleased with this choice and optimistic about Jackson coming on the board.

At the orientation that Jackson and other new trustees attended, David continued to be encouraged. The consultant/

facilitator did an excellent job conveying to the new trustees their roles and responsibilities. There was lots of nodding—confirmation that the new class of trustees "got it" in terms of recognizing the duties and responsibilities and what it meant to be a good trustee. David and other school leaders shook their heads, knowing that there were many current trustees who would benefit from hearing this message!

Soon came the first meeting that included the new trustees. Everyone appropriately welcomed them before getting down to business. David knew that it was inevitable that some shyness would play a part in how these new trustees behaved. All went well until the dreaded executive session. As was her usual inappropriate practice, the chair went around the room seeking comments and concerns. When she got to Jackson, David was hopeful that he would be his usual positive and humorous self in whatever he would say, but such hopes were immediately dashed.

Jackson, in a voice that David had never heard, launched into a tirade about an issue that had absolutely nothing to do with the work of the board. It was an issue that pertained to one of his children, was clearly an operational matter, and had no business even being discussed by the board. David was stunned. Jackson's venom was actually being directed at Jim Conrad, the academic dean. Of course, other trustees had often aimed their weapons at Jim. This infuriated David, who wanted so much to remind them that Jim did not report to the trustees—they had one employee, and it was David Andrews!

This in no way inhibited Jackson, who thought nothing of making his case and doing everything possible to embarrass Jim. As he always did, Jim patiently and clearly responded to Jackson's outburst and, soon afterward, another contentious board meeting came to a close.

Following the meeting David and Jim compared notes as to the meeting in general and Jackson's remarks in particular. They both agreed they had witnessed a side of Jackson that neither had ever seen before. They decided it might just be first-meeting bravado—an attempt to stake his position as a trustee who would be heard, who would be taken seriously.

At the next board meeting, David and Jim waited for the other shoe to drop. Sure enough, when it came time for Jackson to speak, he once again took the opportunity to express his displeasure about another issue that had no reason to be brought before the board. He talked on and on about his wife and his numerous children at the school and how they were suffering because of the failure of some faculty member to do exactly as Jackson had wanted. David looked intently at his shoes while Jim attempted a response to Jackson's ridiculous inquiry.

A few weeks later, David and Jackson were having a pleasant conversation when David suddenly recalled Jackson's behavior at the board meeting. David decided he knew Jackson well enough to bring up the subject of his behavior. David explained that Jackson's comments had been hurtful to him and Jim, and they had further served to undermine both of them in front of other board members. He decided not to make an issue of the actual subject matter—that could wait for another occasion.

Jackson was astonished by this revelation. He expressed doubt that his words and actions could have had the kind of impact David was describing. David made it quite clear that they were both hurt by his remarks. David shared, "Your remarks came across as mean-spirited and suggested that you needed to meet with Jim to discuss your concerns." David was convinced that Jackson was a pretty good guy. Could his attitude, which had become such an issue, be turned around? David and Jim wanted to be optimistic.

In the board meetings that followed, it was clear that Jackson was not a good fit as a board member. Not so much because he disagreed with David and Jim on a range of issues. Disagreeing was fine. It was the lack of civility in his tone that conveyed disrespect. It was also clear that he had become a one-issue trustee, thus causing him to be ineffective in setting a strategic vision for the school's future. He probably did not originally intend to establish himself in this light, but once he got fixated on an issue, there seemed to be no way to alter his thinking. To his credit, Jackson went to see the chair and suggested that he step down. Even Jackson realized he was not being effective. This was a surprising move since most trustees view themselves as invaluable and rarely offer to voluntarily step down.

This would have been an ideal opportunity for board chair Jane Stevens to appoint a new trustee, one with a broader vision of the opportunities and needs of the school. Instead Stevens took the easy way by ignoring his desire to step down. "We need trustees like Jackson Lee," Stevens declared. "His stepping down is not the answer." Again, she had failed to grasp the opportunity to strengthen the board. It was easier to keep a current trustee rather than go to the trouble of finding a replacement. The combination of arrogance and ignorance on the part of the chair was not serving the institution. A trustee with a single focus is not an effective trustee. David knew that a board leader who does not recognize this will ultimately discover his support is eroding.

Chapter 11

MAKING
A DIFFERENCE

"What lies behind us and what lies before us
are tiny matters compared to what lies within us."
—RALPH WALDO EMERSON

In spite of his troubles with the Board of Trustees David was
always cognizant of what his responsibilities and priorities
truly were—to make a difference in the lives of the students
who attended Sanders Academy. He had spoken on this topic on
numerous occasions, including remarks made in several com-
mencement speeches. David had always been convinced that
what truly inspires people is the opportunity to make a difference in the lives of others.

At the invitation of the parent of a Sanders alumnus, David and his wife attended a college football game where the alumnus excelled on the team. When they arrived, they were seated next to another individual, whose two boys had also graduated from Sanders and had done well in college. David was quite fond of this family. He had not seen them in several years but immediately called to mind something the father said to David on the occasion of his oldest son's graduation: "You made a difference in my son's life. It was always obvious that you cared about him. In fact, many parents noticed that you were always there—attending athletic events, concerts, plays, and more." David downplayed his role, but the father insisted: "Leadership—servant leadership—is the tangible demonstration of being a person of responsibility and authority, as well as someone who makes sure they are present and supporting those whom you are responsible for leading. I think it is a rare quality, but one that you possess in abundance."

> David often reflected on the impact he was having—whether or not he made much of a difference.

David often reflected on the impact he was having—whether or not he made much of a difference. He rarely heard expressions of support as shared by this father. It was a compliment he would never forget.

It was certainly something he never heard from trustees. Yes, there were a few supportive trustees, but no one went out of their way to reveal how they felt—unless, of course, it was to express acute criticism. To be sure, David never sought compliments. However, words of praise and affirmation went a long way with David. He was passionate about what he did, but he was even more inspired when someone praised him or a member of his faculty and staff. David was someone who believed one of the most important things you could do to ensure success was to surround yourself with the smartest, most capable people possible.

This premise was somewhat lost on the leadership of the Sanders board. Instead of seeking capable people who loved the school and sought only to advance the mission, new trustees tended to be very much like all of the other trustees.

Chapter 12

PARTNERS
OR CONSPIRATORS?

"Any fool can criticize, condemn, and complain—
and most fools do."
—DALE CARNEGIE

D avid believed that the board of trustees and the administration should have formed a partnership with one another, which was what David had witnessed while serving on the boards of several schools and nonprofit organizations, sometimes in a leadership capacity. The relationship between the board and senior administration was designed to reflect trust, avoid politics and lies and, perhaps most importantly, encourage effective communication between the two entities. This, he realized, was the ideal scenario, a goal at which to aim.

This was not the environment at Sanders Academy. What David found was that all too often trustees were meeting in secret, never including David, and making decisions in the absence of genuine information to support their reason for meeting in the first place. Clearly there existed a lack of trust and respect. Had past experiences been the cause of current circumstances? David was convinced there was a small group of trustees who participated in these activities. These were powerful individuals who were always trying to intimidate—making their wishes known by working behind the scenes to manipulate situations and circumstances to achieve whatever they wanted.

> All too often trustees were meeting in secret, never including David, and making decisions in the absence of genuine information.

David was not so naïve as to believe that this school was the only school or nonprofit organization to suffer from individuals who possessed these characteristics. In other significant ways, these were people of character and integrity. But in the arena of their role as a trustee, they operated in a manner that damaged the work David and his staff were trying to do, damage the school, and damage the experience the students and their parents expected to receive.

What was so unsettling about all of this was that there was no reason for it. In every measurable way the school was moving in the right direction; enrollment, giving, faculty morale, alumni support, and overall reputation of the school were trending up. Was everything perfect? Certainly not. There were numerous issues and challenges. But in every case, Sanders Academy was addressing important issues and constantly trying to improve to ensure that it was the best value in the independent school market. So what was the end game of these trustees who met in secret and were convinced that David Andrews was not doing this or accomplishing that?

The real dispute had much to do with the manner in which David had been selected as head of the school. The search committee had been far from unanimous in its decision, and many of the trustees who had supported another candidate were insistent that David's contract include language that made it almost impossible for him to succeed. David's mistake was signing the contract in the first place. As he reflected back, he wondered, *What did the search consultant share with the search committee that created division and distrust at the outset—those for the candidate selected and those for the candidate not selected? And why didn't the leadership suggest that this, perhaps, was not a good idea?*

Over time this became the dominant issue on which to evaluate David's leadership. In effect, he would be judged based almost completely on one issue—how much money had been raised on his watch. It was unheard of for a leader to be subjected to such a burden or have something so absurd written into his or her contract. The idea that a contract could be built principally around a single issue rather than a balanced and thorough approach to his responsibilities made little sense.

Partners or conspirators—David very much wanted the support and the partnering that resulted from a relationship based on trust and shared vision for the mission at hand. Instead, he had to deal with trustees who met in secret, behind his back, never sharing with him their conversations. He knew that the more effective schools functioned at another level—a level of trust and respect between board and head. It was an issue that clearly was divisive and destructive.

Chapter 13

AN UNEASY ALLIANCE

"As such people achieve influence
within an organization, whenever there is a conflict
between their own interest and the interest
of the organization, their interests will win out."
—Robert Shea

David had served on the board of two independent church-related schools and had worked with many other schools, often but not always K-8 institutions. From the very beginning of independent and Christian schools, the alliance and relationship between church and school effectively served students and families and genuinely made a positive difference in their lives—as long as leadership was not lacking.

David was certainly aware of many different denominational and non-denominational schools that had a wonderful and worthy mission. However, a troubling pattern was emerging where either schools were trying to pull away from their church roots, or churches were trying to exert more control and, in effect, take over the school. Neither situation was healthy, and such patterns were going to bring chaos to these relationships. In a conversation he had with one school head, he learned some very disturbing news about a relationship between the school and the church. The questions for David were, *Where is the leadership? What is the board doing to communicate what is best for the students?* and *What is the most effective way to introduce change into the community?*

The first scenario involved weak churches and strong schools. In many circumstances the church was in place first and at some point the decision was made to add the school, typically seen as an outreach ministry of the church. This model continued to be very effective so long as both church and school thrived. But what happened when there was a shift in the balance? There are any number of reasons why a church becomes the weaker of the two. Certainly economics, demographics, a change in focus or mission all contribute to why the church begins to see their congregations diminish. But the single most important contributing factor that David saw was weak leadership. When the congregation believes weak leadership exists either among professional staff or lay leaders, they will gravitate toward whichever group has a vision that portrays a sense of community.

This environment may be awkward for the school that must be careful of the "tail wagging the dog" syndrome. As David reflected on this issue, his thoughts turned to how a board might react. He asked himself, *What is the church's role in influencing board membership? What do the bylaws say, and can or should they be amended to reflect the new reality?* These are difficult waters to navigate. With thoughtful and intentional leadership coming from the head of school and the school's board of trustees, an atmosphere of teamwork and shared vision can help bring stability until a call to action is needed.

> An atmosphere of teamwork and shared vision can help bring stability until a call to action is needed.

More troubling to David as a school CEO, though, was when a school's financial strength and sustainability grows so great that a jealous, weaker church attempts to take control of the school. Granted, leaders of the founding church may believe that the school "owes" the church by financially helping the church in ways that might be inappropriate. David knew from his experience with accrediting organizations that co-mingling of church and school funds was detrimental to the relationship.

What would happen if the church simply decided that they would "take over" the school and make the decisions about funding and governance? While others would argue it is the right of the church to take whatever action was necessary to safeguard the church, David knew that a controversial situation would arise in which these questions would surface:

1. What percent of the church's membership attend the school?

2. What financial support does the school provide the church?

3. Who has final authority in selecting board members?

4. Does the board leadership need to come from the church?

5. Do leaders of the school have to be members of the host church?

6. Do all board members have to be members of the church?

7. What does this relationship consist of?

8. What is documented about the components of this relationship?

David knew of a school that was about fifteen years old, at which the relationship between the church and the school was working—perhaps not in perfect harmony, but working. All of a sudden, though, church leadership decided to take over the school, with no input from the school's leadership, the board of trustees, or anyone else. When David interviewed the head, he indicated that such a move was uncalled for and put him in a very difficult situation. He was told that he would have to become a member of the church to retain his position as head of the school! David was stunned. How could a school maintain a level of independence in an environment that demanded the head of the school be a member of the church? This was a troubling, about-face maneuver that caused turmoil, unnecessary disruption, and general distraction for students, parents, church members, church leaders, and board members.

There had to be a better way to resolve conflicts such as this. So much emotion was in play. Territorial issues found their way into the discussion. Only through a process of servant leadership would this situation have any chance at resolution. Was there common ground on which the church and the school could replace rancor with reconciliation? Or was this a situation that was simply spinning out of control because no one was willing to step into the gap and proclaim that working together was more important than anything else in order to maintain a healthy, effective school? If this were not possible, many parents might be making other choices for their children's education, and then both church and school would lose.

Chapter 14

WHAT'S YOUR PROBLEM?

"A rumor without a leg to stand on
will get around some other way."
—John Tudor

P arents at independent schools are often wonderful partners
in the education of their children. They are involved, supportive, and communicate effectively with the faculty members
who are teaching their children. The partnership among parents,
teachers, and staff can and should be a hallmark of a great school.
At some schools there are scenarios where this is not the case.
Parents will not know how to resolve certain issues, who to go to,
or how to communicate their concerns. In a well-meaning but

misguided attempt to find solutions, parents will turn to a parent who is also serving as a trustee, believing that part of the role of a school trustee is to listen to and fix parent problems. At an extreme level some parents will simply be seeking information about something that may be none of their business.

There were so many stories that fell into this category, David had to reflect on which provided the best insight to this issue. When he first arrived at Sanders he was almost immediately confronted with an honor code violation that resulted in a decision to expel the students. David thought to himself, *What have I gotten myself into?*

The father of the student was a longtime friend and fellow alumnus of the school. When the father came to David he asked for another chance. David explained that it was a third offense and the Honor Council had made the only decision it could.

For a few days all was calm until one day David's assistant handed him a stack of envelopes with an expression of concern. The envelopes were for each of the trustees and David was expected to mail the letters on behalf of the unhappy parent. David was stunned. It was not his responsibility to mail letters to trustees regarding what was clearly a disciplinary, operational decision and not the business of the trustees. As had been David's practice, he had notified the board by e-mail of the issue without being specific but with the understanding that procedure had been followed. Since it became clear David was not going to deliver the letters, the parent began to make phone calls. Finally the matter came up at the next board meeting. One trustee who understood their role by not becoming involved in such matters made a statement to that effect and the issue was dropped. David was well aware that it could have gone in another direction with trustees weighing in on the issue and telling David what to do to resolve the matter. Fortunately that was not the case—this time.

As a trustee, David had been approached numerous times by parents seeking information, complaining about a faculty member or coach, or any number of matters. David knew that his role as a trustee was not to be the fixer or the problem-solver for these matters. He always listened and was very respectful to the caller. But his answer was often the same: "Thank you for your call, and I appreciate the concern you have regarding this matter. Please know that as a trustee of the school we do not get involved in day-to-day operational matters. Our role is strategy and planning. I would encourage you to address your concern to the [teacher, coach, division head] directly responsible for this issue or the head of school. They will be glad to assist you."

At most independent schools, the governing structure states that the school is under the jurisdiction of an independent board of trustees that has the governing and fiduciary responsibility for the institution. While parents are central and a critical constituency, they are not part of any official governing structure of the school. Unfortunately, this message is one that is not accurately communicated. To be sure, it is difficult to share this message, but many institutions, for a variety of reasons, have chosen to communicate it poorly to families.

> As David talked with school heads, he discovered that an attitude of entitlement exists among many parents.

As David talked with school heads, he discovered that an

attitude of entitlement exists among many parents. The prevailing wisdom of this group says, "Since I am paying tuition, I can seek and also reveal whatever information I deem appropriate or necessary."

The challenge is twofold. On the one hand, how do you communicate to parents in a supportive, non-threatening way what is appropriate to ask and what may be categorized as spreading gossip and rumors? On the other hand, there are many trustees who are also parents, and these individuals are often unable to separate their parental roles from their responsibilities as trustees.

David knew this was a very tricky and treacherous road to travel. Although he confidently knew where he needed to go, he was much less sure of the most effective strategy to get him there. He was certain that communication is central and that it was a journey, not a destination. Both the administration and the board must be in sync regarding the most effective way to communicate with parents. This required the administration to communicate the best way for parents to address matters. Such communication should accomplish the following objectives:

1. Share with parents that the most effective way to resolve an issue is to go directly to that individual and discuss the matter. If the issue is with a teacher, meet with or talk with the teacher.

2. Make it as clear as possible that trustees are not on the board to listen to or resolve complaints or concerns regarding operational matters of the school. This means if parents have a complaint about their son's playing

time on the basketball team, they don't seek the ear of a
trustee to complain about that issue.

3.   Communicate to trustees that they are not in the
     business of acting on the complaints of parents. That is
     the responsibility of the faculty and staff of the school.

4.   Continually train and communicate, year after year.
     There will always be new parents and new trustees who
     must learn this important message and understand
     why this communication is necessary. It has to do
     with hierarchy and tradition and a belief that the most
     effective way to resolve a matter is to address it directly
     with the person and not assume it is someone else's
     responsibility.

Chapter 15

STAFF INFECTION

"Nothing can stop someone with the right mental attitude
from achieving their goal; nothing on earth can help
someone with the wrong mental attitude."
—THOMAS JEFFERSON

David had always been blessed to be surrounded by very
capable people. His staff was composed of individuals with
a passion for excellence that genuinely cared about the future
of Sanders Academy. He had come to trust and respect each of
his senior staff. Some he had hired; some he had inherited. One
in particular concerned David, and he wanted to give this staff
member the benefit of the doubt. Warren Hayes had been on

the staff for several years—many years prior to David's arrival at Sanders Academy.

David was convinced that he could work with Warren and thought he had made his expectations clear. Warren was responsible for development. His knowledge of fundraising was excellent, but his ability to execute was not. He possessed all of the knowledge and technical skills needed for the position. However, his ability to relate to parents, alumni, and other key constituencies was limited. His credentials were excellent. A graduate of Wake Forest, he held numerous certificates indicating his participation in various workshops and continuing education programs. David and Warren worked together for David's first two years as head of Sanders Academy. Though his frustration with Warren was building, David worked hard to show as much support as possible. As far as David knew, Warren understood his relationship with David and his relationship with other members of the board. Warren was close to Stephanie Roland, who chaired the development committee. Warren and Stephanie had been close for many years—years before David's arrival.

While David was somewhat concerned about this relationship, he did not believe it would impact his relationship with either of them. David knew it was important that there be effective communication between trustees and appropriate members of his staff. What he had not foreseen was the relationship between Warren and Stephanie included them both having children at Sanders. Their children became friends and as result of this friendship the parents became very close as well. It became a deep and long-standing relationship. David thought he knew both individuals well. He was wrong.

During his tenure, David had become very good friends with athletic director Mark Martindale, who was a highly respected member of the Sanders community. A basketball player at Furman University, Mark had been at Sanders for a decade. In addition to being the AD, he was also the highly successful varsity basketball coach. When David arrived on campus, he immediately liked Mark and respected his judgment. David knew Mark was all about the students, and the students both loved and respected Mark—some would argue that they also feared him.

During one of their visits, Mark asked David, "Hypothetically, if one of your senior staff members criticized you to a board member, would you want to know about it?"

David was thoughtful in responding, "Yes, this is information I would be very interested in having."

Mark said, "Well, then I have something I need to share with you." Over the next thirty minutes, Mark told David some very disturbing news. "A trustee has come to me with news he was having trouble believing. Apparently Warren Hayes went to Stephanie Roland and complained about you—suggesting that you are a poor leader and not suitable to lead Sanders Academy. I assured this trustee that you were an effective and capable leader and not only was Warren absolutely wrong, but it was inappropriate for Stephanie not to have come to you to discuss this matter."

Needless to say, David was stunned. He related to Mark, "I am really surprised that Warren would do this. Although we have our disagreements, I have always tried to be supportive of him. What especially surprises me is that Stephanie would not come to me and, at the very least, want to hear my side of the story."

Mark then commented, "Some of the complaints Warren had

against you I found to be petty and ridiculous, having nothing to do with your leadership style."

David then asked Mark for his advice on what was clearly insubordination by a staff member and misconduct by a trustee. "I thought I had an excellent relationship with Stephanie. I am truly disappointed that she does not understand that as a trustee, it is her responsibility to come to me immediately. Her first question to Warren should have been, 'Have you discussed this with David?' What do you think I should do?"

David had read and attended enough conferences to know that Warren could have argued that he didn't come to him directly for fear of retaliation or retribution. However, Stephanie had no such excuse. Why had she not come to David directly to discuss the issue? What had happened to the time-honored concept of David being the only employee of the board? A staff member seeking out board members to complain about the head or trustees talking to other trustees about the head—this revealed an environment of mistrust that could potentially cripple the school. Circumstances such as these have very serious consequences. They are not isolated but rather have a ripple effect that creates distrust and uncertainty.

Following additional conversations, David decided the best course of action would be to seek the wisdom of a board member who was also a past chair of the board. A few weeks later he arranged a meeting and had lunch with this trustee. David described in as much detail as possible the circumstances and the situation involving a member of his staff and the two trustees— the trustee who reported the incident to Mark and the trustee who heard the complaint from Warren. David asked for input and advice from this respected member of the board: "I am concerned with what I consider to be insubordination and a lack of communication from the two trustees involved in this situation. I have one trustee who is listening to a member of the staff and then not telling me anything. And on top of that I have another trustee who listens to Stephanie and then tells another member of the staff. It is this staff member that shared all of this with me. This situation does not bode well for my relationship with these board members and this staff member."

The trustee listened carefully to David and then shared his thoughts: "I recognize your concern with all of this. I consider this insubordination on the part of Warren. He has clearly gone behind your back, having never come to you in the first place. Seeking out a trustee to complain to and the trustee not coming to you directly is beyond my understanding. I think you need to confront Warren and indicate that this type of behavior will not be tolerated. Quite frankly, your ability to trust Warren has been drastically compromised. Personally, I don't see how he can continue on your staff. You will need to cautiously monitor this situation. The trustee state of affairs is also very troubling. I thought—perhaps assumed—that our trustees understood how to respond to such situations. Apparently, some do not."

David came away from the meeting with mixed emotions.

These trustees had neglected to adhere to the principles of good practice, failing to call to mind that they had only one employee.

On the one hand, his view of the matter had been confirmed. This was patently a case of defiance on the part of the staff member and an obvious lack of understanding on the part of the two trustees who failed to report the incident to David. He reflected that these trustees had neglected to adhere to the principles of good practice, failing to call to mind that they had only one employee and that employee was David Andrews. David considered what his next move should be and the most appropriate timetable on which to take any action.

David decided that he should approach a former head of the school about how to resolve the situation. He had become well-acquainted with Stan Lealand. Stan had been head of Sanders for several years before moving on to become president of his alma mater, a very good boarding/day school with a distinguished past and a most promising future. Everyone at Sanders Academy hated to see him leave. David trusted his views and looked forward to the visit. He knew Stan to be a good listener. David also knew that Stan knew everyone involved. He figured this knowledge would prove to be very helpful.

A few days later the two men met to discuss the situation and how to proceed. David spent several minutes describing the events in order to give Stan the clearest picture possible. He concluded his remarks by asking Stan, "Have you been in communication with Warren or know anything about what I have just shared with you?"

Stan quickly indicated he had not communicated with Warren in several months and was not aware that he had spoken to a trustee. "I spoke with him several months ago, and I had the impression he was not happy. He didn't say why he was unhappy and I certainly would never have encouraged him to speak to a trustee without first speaking to you. Perhaps your expectations for Warren are different than mine and he is having trouble adjusting to the change in leadership."

David thought about this for a moment and then asked, "What do you suggest that I do? How can I trust someone on my staff who would do what he has done?"

Stan offered, "I would suggest that you meet with Warren and try to determine what the issue is—why he is dissatisfied with his job, or unhappy with you."

"I suppose you are right," David said. "There really is no alternative other than to talk with him. I don't necessarily want him to know that I am aware he went to a trustee to express concerns about me."

Soon after his meeting with Stan, David arranged to get together with Warren. When they met, the discussion covered a range of topics before David finally got around to the primary reason for their meeting. David began, "Warren, I have a feeling that you either are not happy in your position or you are upset with me. I would like to talk about this. Please tell me if you are angry about something I have done. Is there something you would like for me to do differently? Please be candid with me." Then David was silent, waiting for Warren to respond.

After a moment Warren sort of shook his head and said, "No, nothing really. I would like to be included when you are discussing possible fundraising projects. It seems you have communicated a few times with others about possible fundraising projects and have not included me in those discussions."

David responded, "That's it? Are you sure nothing else is bothering you? If there is something, now is the time to come forward. I understand your concern about not being included in conversations about potential projects. I will try to do a better job on this matter. The fact is, I try to seek out those who can assist with specific projects. There are certain people here who have great instincts and are excellent fundraisers. That has always been the way I have operated—it has nothing to do with you."

After Warren departed, David could not believe what he had just heard—or rather what he had not heard. Warren certainly made no indication of having spoken with a trustee. Further, his only complaint was not having been included in a couple of meetings. In reality, David did not want Warren in these meetings because he brought little value to the discussion. Plus, he knew that that there were many across campus who had little respect for the job Warren was doing. David recognized this was becoming a growing problem throughout campus. Warren made almost no attempt to be a part of the campus community. Perhaps he had at one time but certainly not while David was there. He attended no events and seemed to make little effort to be a part of anything. In hindsight David wished he had taken the advice of another trustee who had encouraged David to build his own team, get the people in place that he wanted.

David knew that he needed Warren to be engaged and a vital part of what was going on. This was critical to building relationships with various constituencies of the school—parents, alumni, faculty and staff, other friends, and, of course, students. Why didn't Warren see this as a natural consequence, an obvious extension, of his work? This was akin to Fundraising and Advancement 101. Plus, it should be an enjoyable component of the job—the opportunity to get to know people who cared about and were already connected to the school. To David, if you chose this career path then you would understand how important this is to the success of your fundraising—and friend-raising—efforts.

Fundraising is much more than understanding the techniques and theories behind the profession. It is the ability to implement the program, set a goal and recognize what is required to achieve it, work as a team to accomplish what is expected, and have the passion and commitment to ensure the successful completion of tasks. Perhaps most essential is having an optimistic attitude and confidence to believe in yourself. David was beginning to grasp how critical one's attitude is in achieving one's goals.

In the end Warren stayed and continued to do an adequate job. David should have made a change and the fact that he did not reflected a leadership weakness on his part. The combination of being insubordinate while only doing an average job should have been enough to warrant a change. David thought he could turn the situation around. But that was foolish thinking on his part.

Chapter 16

WHAT'S IN IT FOR ME?

"A man wrapped in himself makes
a very small package."
—BENJAMIN FRANKLIN

David knew that the cast of characters on the board was interesting, to say the least, but there was one trustee he thought he could trust—his boyhood friend Ralph Benton. Ralph had been a long-time member of the board. He was one of the few members who continued on the board long after his children had graduated. David assumed Ralph stayed on the board to protect family interests (his son worked in the admissions office and his daughter-in-law was a member of the faculty).

Soon after David had been hired, Ralph came to him and requested his assistance in getting his son, Ben, hired. David respected Ralph, an esteemed attorney who was very successful at his trade. He could argue with the best of them and was usually on the winning side of most every discussion. He was a man who was not afraid to ask for what he wanted, which he usually got. David agreed to look into the matter and recommend Ben, a Sanders alumnus and a very capable young man. David made sure that Ben was interviewed. Over the course of the search process Ralph contacted David on several occasions to determine the status of Ben's application. In the end Ben was hired. Ralph was pleased but was reserved in thanking David for his part in the process. David did not ask to be thanked but thought it odd considering how heavily he had been lobbied by Ralph. Would Ben have been hired under other circumstances? Perhaps—but David's involvement in the hiring process could not be dismissed.

It wasn't long after this episode that Ralph once again approached David seeking his assistance in the hiring of Ben's wife, Alecia, for a position on the Sanders faculty. And once again David closely monitored the situation to ensure his long-time friend was happy. David would certainly admit this was not the most effective way to hire someone, but he rationalized his role by saying that these were good people who cared about Sanders and would do a good job.

Trustee and friend Ralph did not stop at personnel matters regarding his family members. If he wanted it, if he thought it was in his or his family's best interest, he asked for it and expected it. The more Ralph leveraged their relationship to get his way, the further the two grew apart as friends. No request bothered

David more, though, than when Ralph took up sides for a Sanders student.

The son of a close friend of Ralph's had been suspended for a very serious honor code violation. Of all the reasons for maintaining separation between administration and board, the greatest had to do with disciplinary issues. This made absolutely no difference to Ralph Benton. He did not hesitate to call David and express his opinion—and disagreement over the decision regarding his friend's son. He pleaded this student's case, arguing, "He is a good student who has not been in trouble before. He deserves consideration for who he is and who his family is." David mostly listened. What else could he do with someone who talks all the time and is obviously fascinated by the sound of his own voice? David had communicated with the board on the matter, and further conversation with an individual trustee was unnecessary.

Ralph always expected special treatment but would always be the first to say he never required nor received any special consideration. But Ralph was the kind of person who complained if he did not get his way.

There was no doubt in David's mind that Ralph considered himself a good trustee. He was successful and respected in his career. Surely that must translate into being a good trustee. He was on the board of several other organizations. It only stood to reason that his opinion was a highly sought-after commodity. What he failed to realize was that his true role and value as a board member had nothing to do with any of this. It never occurred to him that what he was doing was inappropriate and unacceptable. But David was trapped. Since he had no support from the board chair, there was nowhere to go to express his concerns.

Ralph had turned out to be a classic meddler—an individual who sees the world only through his own eyes. An individual who is seldom wrong and never in doubt. He had no boundaries and without a doubt took advantage of his position as a board member. Not only had he strained a lifelong friendship, he

> Ralph had turned out to be a classic meddler. He had no boundaries and without a doubt took advantage of his position as a board member.

was undermining David's leadership position and hindering his ability to effectively guide the school.

In public, Ralph often expressed support for David, but he privately conferred with other trustees to express his disappointment with and, perhaps, distrust of David. He was always looking for an angle. It was always, "What's in it for me?"

Years later, when David's time at Sanders was coming to an end, there were many opportunities when Ralph could have and should have come to his defense. But Ralph was too much in the grips of other trustee colleagues who wanted David gone— regardless of how irrational that was. Ralph never failed to ask David for favors, never failed to meddle, never failed to speak up when he thought a member of his immediate family wanted something. But when David needed support, Ralph was nowhere to be found. He never spoke up for David, never expressed his disagreement with those who sought David's departure, never defended David to those irrational trustees with their unrealistic expectations. Like other trustees, he expected to be in the know on everything. He was unconcerned and unfamiliar with best practices. He was the model trustee—just ask him!

PART TWO

MIKE

"The secret of joy in work
is contained in one word—excellence.
To know how to do something well is to enjoy it."
—PEARL S. BUCK

Chapter 17

A CHANGE
FOR THE BETTER

"As any change must begin somewhere,
it is the single individual who will experience it
and carry it through. The change must indeed come
from an individual; it might be any one of us."
—CARL JUNG

D avid and the senior team at Sanders Academy welcomed
the announcement of Jane Stevens's retirement. The chair
for far too many years, her leadership was lacking in so many
important ways. Her ability to inspire other board members
was practically nonexistent. She allowed individual board members to meddle, bully, and threaten administrative leaders of the

85

school. Communicating and partnering with David was in short supply. She encouraged and participated in secret meetings among the executive committee and others on the board to raise whatever complaint this group thought appropriate. She was the chief architect of an atmosphere of distrust and fear. In short, she possessed almost none of the leadership qualities that were so badly needed by a board chair. David hoped that the board would pick someone with whom David could work.

One of the numerous problems with the structure of the Sanders Academy board was there was no clear-cut line of succession to become chair. The person who served as vice-chair might become chair, but this was not necessarily the case. In other words, the executive committee could select anyone on the board to recommend to the full board as to who should become the next chair. David's counsel was not sought nor was he given an opportunity to offer any suggestions. David realized that there were those who thought this to be solely a decision by the board. However, he believed very much that the board and he should be genuine partners in moving the organization forward—communicating when possible in the best interest to ensure the most effective people were in place.

Mike Riley, a board member who had served two terms, emerged as the frontrunner. He was very different than the previous chair. Mike was a high-energy person who was confident, encouraging, and always demonstrated a positive attitude. He was someone who had built a business and sold it for millions.

Extremely friendly, Mike looked like a candidate that Sanders badly needed. Mike was not afraid of change and recognized that the school was poised for changes that would have a positive impact. In addition—and not lost on anyone—Mike was both extremely wealthy and extremely generous. Although David was not involved in the decision, not even in a consultation role, everyone knew he wanted Mike to fill the position. But since David had grown accustomed to *not* getting what he wanted, he was quite surprised when Mike was elected chair of the Sanders Academy board of trustees. David knew he could work with Mike and also knew that Mike would be an excellent fit for the school. The two men shared an entrepreneurial belief that moving forward had much to do with a number of factors, including:

1. Building enrollment—both through increasing retention and adding new students.

2. Increasing overall giving to the school primarily through enhancing the annual fund program.

3. Implementing strategic marketing efforts designed around branding and messaging.

4. Enhancing the appearance of the campus and upgrading facilities through projects that are notably impactful while also economically manageable.

5. Seeking ways to manage expenses without sacrificing people or programs.

Mike Riley and David Andrews were on the same page, and David looked to the future with an optimism that he had not felt in years.

Chapter 18

POWER PLAY

"Awards become corroded;
friends gather no dust."
—Jesse Owens

Sanders Academy had a storied history that included success in all aspects of the school—academics, the arts, and athletics. It was a school that took great pride in its balanced approach to the educational experience—what the school described and frequently articulated as "educating the whole Child." As with so many schools, football was all-important, and Sanders had a winning tradition. Scott Holt, the football coach, was legendary and had a legion of followers who considered him to be one of the best high school football coaches in the state, if not the country.

During David's tenure, this "coach for the ages" decided it was time to retire. This surprised David, because he and everyone else in the community had thought his retirement was several years into the future. Word of Coach Holt's retirement soon spread like wildfire, and it seemed as though everyone—whether connected to Sanders or not—expressed their opinion as to why this great man was stepping down. What had caused Coach Holt to retire? Surely there was someone to blame for this calamity. David remained positive throughout the early days of this news, believing that Sanders would find a suitable replacement. He was confident he enjoyed the support of new trustee chair, Mike Riley.

David knew (or, more accurately, assumed) that there would be factions of the board who would want to take control of the search for the next head football coach, or allow Coach Holt to be directly involved in picking his successor. David felt that meeting with Riley was necessary to clarify matters and to ensure that they were on the same page.

Sure enough, it didn't take long before a contingency from the board approached the chair and strongly suggested that Coach Holt be given the honor of naming his successor. The idea that David was their only employee and that all personnel responsibility rested with him was completely foreign to them. For these trustees, it was a matter of taking control of the situation and placing responsibility for this hire with Coach Holt. These board members

A contingency from the board approached the chair and strongly suggested that Coach Holt be given the honor of naming his successor.

argued that David Andrews knew little about coaching and would not have the connections or the networking skills needed to hire the best new coach.

Coach Holt had unprecedented success at Sanders. His tenure had included numerous state championships, players who excelled in college, and even a few who enjoyed success in professional football. There were many across all constituencies who firmly believed Coach Holt had both the right and responsibility to name his successor, or at least to be directly involved in the process. After all, they argued, who knew the football program or the school better than Coach Holt? Who else could possibly be trusted with a decision as important as this one?

When David and Mike Riley met to discuss the matter, they were each able to state their positions and decide on a strategy for moving forward. David, who held the strongest possible belief about how best to address the matter—best for the school and best for the students—began the meeting: "Mike, while I understand and respect those trustees and many others who believe Coach Holt should be involved in the search for his successor, I do not believe this is the direction we should pursue. All hiring ultimately is my responsibility, and this position is no different than any other personnel matter. Don't get me wrong, I am well aware of the place of athletics here—especially football—but we need to follow the same procedures we'd adhere to for any other open staff position. I realize that there are some trustees who view this as a unique situation, but such involvement and interference will only set a precedent that will have consequences we cannot begin to grasp."

Mike listened intently, nodding his head repeatedly.

David continued, "If this is indeed a power play—an opportunity for the board to demonstrate its importance and influence over the administration—then we have a much greater challenge. There is a lot at risk here, and we need to put a stake in the ground together and present to the entire Sanders Academy where we stand. For this to work, for this to enable the school to move forward in the most positive manner possible, your support is a critical component." David had made his case as best he could. Now was the time for Mike to demonstrate some genuine board leadership. David held his breath.

The new chair of the board made his position crystal clear. "David, I completely concur with everything you have just shared with me. When it comes to personnel matters, the board has hired you, and this decision is yours. You may choose to collaborate with anyone or any group you believe will be helpful. Further, I will make evident to all board members my position. I think going in any other direction is a slippery slope that we as trustees have no business going down."

David expressed his deep appreciation and gratitude for the manner in which the new chair was discharging his duties. He knew this would not be the last conversation on the subject, but he was now well-prepared for what might happen next.

David decided the best way to proceed would be to have an advisory group that would give him input, similar to a search committee. While he knew this input would be helpful, he also knew that the final decision—and responsibility—was his alone.

Before meeting with his advisory team, he needed to first have a conversation with Coach Holt, and he was sure it would not be an easy one. It was important, though, that the coach understood and, hopefully, respected the process the school would be following. David began the conversation by expressing his appreciation for the way he had represented the school, the manner in which he worked with students, and the way in which he connected and communicated with families. Although David mentioned the success Coach Holt's teams had experienced and how grateful he was for the football program's positive impact on the school, he did not dwell on this.

Coach Holt was disappointed in the way the process was going to unfold. He obviously didn't agree with David having the responsibility of hiring the next football coach. He tried to argue, but David stated, "Coach, I know you don't agree with this process, but this is a personnel matter, and all personnel issues are ultimately my responsibility. I am counting on you to accept this and work with me in moving forward to find the next football coach for Sanders Academy. You, more than anyone, know the value of the team concept. I need you to be a part of the team that does what is best for Sanders. I hope I can count on you."

As a result of the attitude and partnership between board chair, Mike Riley, and president, David Andrews, Sanders Academy went through a very successful search. They found a great fit for Sanders and someone who shared the school's values and embraced the mission.

Several trustees lobbied hard for a very different process. Both Mike and David respected their view; however, they both knew allowing them to run things would set the wrong precedent regarding future personnel decisions. David had demonstrated true leadership and had worked closely with the board chair to build a process that would ensure that it was obvious all personnel matters were ultimately the president's responsibility.

Further, this episode revealed that the board has an important role in the school's future. However, that role does not include deciding who the next football coach is going to be. This was a critical test, and David was pleased with how it had been resolved.

Chapter 19

VALUE
AND RELEVANCY

"A committee is a group that
keeps minutes and loses hours."
—MILTON BERLE

How many board meetings each year is the right number? Does having more or less meetings make a difference in a school's effectiveness? Is the governance impacted based on the frequency of meetings? These are questions that David and every school and nonprofit executive ponder from time to time.

When Mike Riley began his time as chair of the board, he wanted to discuss these issues with David. Sanders had a history of meeting six times a year. It was important to Mike not to meet for the sake of meeting. Mike wanted to be sure that the staff was not spending too much of their time preparing for board meetings and more time making sure that Sanders was the best school it could be.

David had studied and discussed this issue with a number of leaders in order to better understand the relationship between the number of board meetings and the effectiveness of the organization. He discovered that many boarding schools met only twice a year. This model seemed to work since many board members often traveled from great distances to attend meetings. David reflected that under these circumstances there had to exist a high level of trust between the board and the head of school.

At the other end of the spectrum, there were many boards that met monthly, either throughout the calendar year or the school year. Often these boards tended to be smaller in number and with fewer standing committees. David observed that because of the numerous meetings, the staff spent considerable time preparing for and following up from the meetings. While he could not necessarily determine if this impacted the effectiveness of the school, what he did note is that the head of school had significant support from the board—recognizing the importance of "the board has one hire" mentality.

The other two most likely scenarios were boards that met every other month or quarterly. Personally, David liked these two models because they allowed for much more interaction and relationship with the staff and other boards members while still safeguarding the idea of not prying into the day-to-day operational areas of the school. David was very cognizant of the board's responsibility for financial sustainability, but there must be a high level of trust the staff would effectively and productively do their job.

Tradition is important and has its place in a school or any organization. The expression "If it ain't broke, don't fix it" is also one not to be ignored. However, reviewing what you are doing in an effort to get better at what you do is also a helpful way to look at your circumstances.

> Reviewing the number of meetings would inevitably result in reviewing the bylaws as well, and a strategic review of the Sanders Academy bylaws was in order.

David was not a proponent of the worn-out idea "This is the way we have always done it." This anti-change approach was often code for "We are not receptive to change." There was a place for strategic thinking and discussing of these issues to establish the best possible way to function.

The issue of meetings was somewhat difficult to change without taking a look at the bylaws to assess the level of flexibility. In most cases the number of meetings and the name and function of standing committees is specifically covered in the organization's bylaws. David realized that reviewing the number of meetings would inevitably result in reviewing the bylaws as well, and a strategic review of the Sanders Academy bylaws was in order. This document had not been updated in many years, and even if nothing changed as a result of the board's review, at least everyone had the opportunity to refresh their memories and then agree to change things or leave them alone.

David understood that discussions revolving around process are important but that they do not necessarily reflect the value and relevancy of the school. Meetings are an expression of communication, and communication is central in articulating mission, vision, strategy, and much more. It was the structure and outcome of meetings that revealed results. But more than that, a positive attitude from leaders establishes an atmosphere in which everyone believes the board is doing all it can to ensure that better days are ahead for the school.

PART THREE

"No good deed goes unpunished."
—OSCAR WILDE

Chapter 20

MOVING ON

"From the sublime to the ridiculous
is but a step."
—Napoleon

D avid and Mike exemplified the ideal relationship between a head and a board chair. It was clear they connected and communicated effectively. It was the type of partnership that moves organizations forward. This "lack of conflict" between these two leaders would immensely benefit the students and faculty of Sanders Academy. What were the characteristics that made this relationship so effective?

1.   *Communication and collaboration.* It was clear to
     David that Mike had communicated and collaborated

successfully with others throughout his career. This characteristic served him in effectively collaborating with David as well as the board. The idea of working together was a key ingredient to success.

2. *Respect.* David and Mike respected each other in large measure because they both were very much aware of one another's capabilities and desire to work hard.

3. *Trust.* They trusted one another—period. Because there was respect, there was trust. David was candid and always openly and honestly communicated with Mike on issues of mutual interest or concern. There were no secret meetings, no clandestine communications regarding the school that Mike would allow to take place.

4. *Support.* David always knew he had Mike's support. Though they might disagree on an issue or how to resolve a concern, David was always aware that Mike would not allow or tolerate unprofessional and unethical behavior from any board member.

5. *Shared vision.* Both knew that ultimately their reason for doing what they did had everything to do with ensuring the student experience was the best possible and that the future was as secure as it could be.

6. *Attitude.* Above all, David celebrated having a relationship with someone who was positive and believed that the people with whom he interacted also wanted do things the right way.

7. *Leadership.* Both saw their roles as leading by example and through serving. Their goal was to surround themselves with incredibly talented and capable people and then support their work. This was David's goal with staff and faculty; it was Mike's goal with the board of trustees.

What an exciting proposition. David mistakenly thought, or undoubtedly wished, that he would have the opportunity to work with Mike for several years. He had tried for years to work with the previous chair, only to be bullied and threatened the entire time.

With Mike as the chair, board meetings were actually fun. Mike demonstrated leadership qualities that inspired the board. He had the ability to bring out the best in everyone. Everyone functioned at the highest possible level because they believed in Mike's capacity to accomplish whatever he set out to do.

It was unmistakable that David enjoyed the full support of the new board chair. Board members knew this as well as the senior staff. Mike was aware of the recent history of all types of unprofessional behavior that the board had exhibited. No more. The new sheriff in town would not tolerate it. Mike was all about healthy debate and discussion, but he was not about demeaning arguments in which the board attempted to demonize David or a member of his senior staff. When describing his philosophy, Mike stated, "We are going to be about best practices. One of the very best ways we can ensure that our school can live out its mission and safeguard its future is for the board to demonstrate to everyone that it desires to work as a cohesive group of volunteers who understand their role and have only one agenda—empowering Sanders Academy to be the best school possible."

Before Mike took over, trust had been lacking among the Sanders board. The atmosphere had consisted of a group of individuals who were used to getting their way and unable to function as a unified group. Therefore, it had been virtually impossible to move the school forward. Mike was aware that part of his task as chair was to:

1. Encourage the board to work together.

2. Insist that interactions and relationships be not only civil but also positive as in having a positive attitude even when disagreements arise.

3. Position the head as a leader worthy of respect and trust.

4. Ensure that the board focus on core responsibilities of mission, strategy, policy, and planning.

5. Resist every temptation to meddle, bully, or threaten any member of the senior staff.

One day things began to change, though. Mike had been the chair for approximately one year when he called David and asked to meet. David had a feeling something wasn't right and had been concerned about him. He had noticed a subtle change in Mike over the last several weeks, how he seemed distracted and less enthusiastic in serving as chair.

David didn't know what the meeting was about, but he was anxious to hear what he had to share. Mike began by being very complimentary of David. "You have done a great job, and I genuinely appreciate your passion for what you do. It is apparent to all of our constituencies—faculty, staff, students, parents, and alumni—that you desire to uphold the traditions that cement Sanders Academy's unique heritage and to encourage any change that will make it an even stronger school. I apologize for the treatment you have received from several board members, and I hope that kind of conduct is a thing of the past." David was flattered by these comments but knew there was more to why Mike and he were meeting.

Mike continued, "I am sorry to tell you this, but I have to step down as chair of the board. In fact, I need to leave the board altogether. I am beginning a new business relationship that will mean significant travel, and I will soon be relocating to another part of the country."

David tried very hard not to show his profound disappointment. He pleaded with Mike and made every effort not to make it about him. "Mike, I am obviously disappointed but wish you the best. Is there no way you could work something out at least for the remainder of the year? We only have three more board meetings this year. It would be a huge help if you could preside until the end of the school year." David knew this was a long shot.

Mike made his position very clear: "David, I know you are disappointed, and I am, too, because I've really enjoyed working with you. But for business and personal

David anticipated that his chances of working effectively with the new chair were not good, because he knew whom the board would likely appoint.

reasons, it is extremely important that I take on this new responsibility in another part of the country and do so right away."

David knew the transition to another board chair would be

difficult. He also anticipated that his chances of working effectively with the new chair were not good, because he knew whom the board would likely appoint.

As David expected, the board elected Calvin Dunn as the next chair of the board. Dunn possessed several classic traits that David loathed. Dunn was a meddler. He was the type who needed to be in the middle of everything. He always found some excuse to be on campus, usually in business manager Dan Reagan's office . . . or in David's office. He had a quirky personality and considered himself an expert on almost any subject. Everything that happened on campus was Dunn's business. He completely ignored the idea that the board should not be involved in the school's day-to-day activities. To him, involvement was an opportunity to put his stamp on the school.

One of Dunn's most unflattering characteristics is that he talked about others behind their backs. He was overly critical of everyone. No one was as smart or savvy as Calvin Dunn. He criticized other trustees, including people who had been very generous to the school, past trustee chairs, and anyone else who did not measure up to his standards of perfection. This was troubling to David as he pondered, *How do I confront someone who is my boss when he is overtly critical of many whom I respect—including Mike Riley?*

David considered himself a builder—a leader who had a vision for what the future could be. He was responsible for enrollment, fundraising, marketing, branding, communications, and financial management. To Dunn, the world was only about financial restraint. Investment in physical facilities, programs, or people was considered marginal and mostly unnecessary. Dunn was not someone who wanted to build but rather someone who embraced cutbacks—cutting salaries, cutting expenses, cutting the budget, cutting everything. No two people could be more opposite.

When the two men first met, David knew this would not work. Dunn wanted more board meetings, more executive committee meetings, and more finance committee meetings. He even wanted to bring back executive sessions. He basically wanted to be more involved in ways that were not only unnecessary, but also principally inappropriate. Dunn's idea of a head of school was someone who was more like an accountant or corporate CEO—a person who first and foremost looked at everything through the lens of financial controls. David understood the importance of making sure the school was solvent, sustainable, and relevant. Dunn desired a one-dimensional head of school, but David knew an effective leader does so much more than just cut expenses.

Calvin Dunn was not a collaborator. Some may have described him as a problem solver, but his leadership style was to wear you down until you accepted his way of thinking. David had to admit there were occasions Calvin had been instrumental in resolving matters, but for the most part his approach was to intervene when he should have delegated tasks to David, who would have then assigned specific action steps to staff members. Calvin Dunn didn't care that the board had only one employee—president David Andrews—and he never respected David nor tried to build this relationship. Last, but not least, Dunn had an enormous ego. He wanted the credit for everything, and he criticized others who did not recognize his greatness.

Sadly, David saw no alternative but to step down. He was certain Calvin did not view him as the type of leader the school needed. David was in his eighth year as president, and it had been an extremely difficult tenure—probably the most challenging and stressful time of his life, with the exception of the year under the enlightened leadership of Mike Riley. He took comfort in knowing he did everything he could, worked as hard as possible, and achieved amazing results. His leadership had resulted in record enrollment, record financial support, incredible academic achievement by students, increased faculty morale, and a positive atmosphere among every one of the school's constituencies. In the end, though, none of that seemed to matter.

David knew that he could not be effective if he was not wanted and respected or if his leadership was not valued. His time at Sanders Academy was over. He should have fought back and challenged the leadership of the board, but it was not David's style to be confrontational. He was sure that such action would hurt the reputation of the school, and he did not want that to happen. It was time to move on—time to get happy again. In a single step he had gone from the sublime (empowering leadership of Mike Riley) to the ridiculous (the leaderless meddling of Calvin Dunn).

David and his wife, Karen, discussed the situation at great length since it certainly affected their future in dramatic ways. In the end, she agreed with David that the best thing for him to do was resign. "It is time to consider our next adventure," she told him. "Our children are grown, and our options are numerous. We are a team, and I believe we should make this change." David had forgotten how blessed he was to be married to perhaps the most understanding woman in the world.

David scheduled a meeting with Calvin to inform him of his decision. He did not look forward to it. When the two men met, Calvin anticipated what was coming and beat David to the punch by stating a change in leadership was warranted. David was stunned and sat silently as the new board chair articulated his vision as to what he thought was essential for the next president. He outlined a scenario in which he wanted to look at the corporate model, believing that someone with strong financial credentials and experiences such as an accountant or CFO would be best suited for the job. He outlined an environment that included substantial cuts to programs, salaries, and facilities. David thought to himself, "God help the individual who comes to this position and has to work with this man." After thirty minutes of outlining the new day that was coming, Calvin thanked David for his service.

Throughout the entire meeting, David was given no opportunity to speak, no opportunity to respond, and no opportunity to defend himself or the actions he had taken. It was indicative of the type of leadership Dunn would unleash on the school—extensive talking and very little listening.

What an ending to a time more difficult than anything anyone other than his devoted wife could imagine. In the months and years after he left Sanders Academy, David couldn't find the right words to describe the environment and circumstances he faced during his eight years as school president. When he alluded to his predicament when speaking with other school heads and nonprofit leaders, they mostly shook their heads not really comprehending the depth of despair that David had experienced. David was left with many questions:

- Why had the board taken on the posture of bullying and threatening?

- Why had the leadership allowed the trustees to behave in such a destructive manner?

- Why had the chair failed to discipline the board when so many trustees were obviously out of control?

- Why had orientation and continuing education opportunities completely gone ignored?

- Why had the chair disregarded David's requests to better communicate with one another?

- Why had David failed to work more effectively with the board, given that he himself had been a board member?

These questions and many more would haunt David in the weeks and months to come. He could not escape the notion that he had been set up to fail. His fate was sealed years earlier when the board adopted evaluation goals that no one could accomplish. Hindsight being so clear, David had wished with all his heart that he would have had the courage to say no—no to such a flawed process and no to the unrealistic expectations none of the prior presidents had ever had to endure. The fundamental unfairness weighed heavy on his heart. He had failed. He had let others down. He had let his family down. And he had let himself down. Perhaps most of all, he had let down the school he loved and cared about so much.

In the days ahead he would begin to put into perspective his years at Sanders Academy. There were numerous fond memories, but there were countless memories that were painful. What could he learn from this experience? More importantly, what in all of these experiences could he teach others? One factor became clear—it was acutely important for David to use these experiences to warn school leaders, nonprofit CEOs and EDs–*and* board members—about the dangers and challenges that these groups may face and address every day. These events must be revealed, must be shared, and must help ensure a new day for schools and nonprofit organizations. The relationship between the staff leadership and the board must be built on trust, mutual respect, a positive attitude, and a belief that there is too much at stake for anything less than the very best.

Chapter 21

FAITH
AND RESOLVE

"Your success and happiness lies in you.
Resolve to keep happy and your joy and you shall
form an invincible host against difficulties."
—HELEN KELLER

Above all, David knew that he had been blessed in count-less ways. His career had included numerous leadership, teaching, consulting, and speaking opportunities all across the country as well as internationally. David was a man of faith and was confident God had a plan for him. After stepping down from Sanders Academy, he knew he needed to find ways to help schools and nonprofit organizations build stronger relationships between the governing board and senior leadership of the organization. Here were some of the questions that arose from his tenure as a school head:

- What should be the new standard for governance and leadership?

- What had he discovered about the bond between head of school, senior staff, and board of trustees?

- What innovation and creativity could improve these relationships?

- What mattered most to the organization's sustainability and future?

- What had he learned from colleagues, conferences, and conversations that would give him insight in utilizing what he knew, what he learned, and what he understood?

- What knowledge had he gained from other leadership experiences during his career that could translate over to the private education and nonprofit worlds?

David knew there had to be a better way. Innovation, communication, and collaboration would be at the center of a new model. Process, people, personalities, and power had to be right for the model to work.

> David knew there had to be a better way. Process, people, personalities, and power had to be right for the model to work.

The past eight years had been a challenge. Filled with blessings and frustration, whatever David had learned, he was determined to use his experiences to benefit school heads, nonprofit CEOs, and also those who serve on boards—especially board members. If he could do that, then he knew what he had gone through was for a greater purpose.

Chapter 22

LESSONS LEARNED

"Try not to become a man of success
but rather to become a man of value."
—**Albert Einstein**

In the months following his resignation from Sanders Academy, David began journaling about his experiences, feelings, and ideas for leading a better private school or nonprofit organization. The more he wrote, the more his thoughts started to take form as lessons that he could share with others as well as use himself were he given another opportunity to lead another organization.

While there are other things that could be learned, David believed these twenty lessons were the most important ones that would have the greatest impact:

Lesson 1: *The search committee must be unanimous in its decision to hire someone.* One of the most detrimental components to his ability to work effectively with the board revolved around the fact that the search committee was unable to reach a clear-cut decision. In David's opinion, search consultants must communicate as clearly

> David believed these twenty lessons were the most important ones that would have the greatest impact.

as possible that the search committee ultimately stands behind the majority's decision regardless of the outcome of the initial voting. Otherwise they must resign from the board if they feel they will not be able to support the candidate selected. If the candidate does not have the complete support of the search committee, the full board will raise questions about the process, and rightly so. Should a new search be conducted? This is a possibility if the board cannot fully endorse the choice of the search committee. A split committee will lead to a split board, which will lead to a dysfunctional organization. Coming out of the gate without unanimity will not serve the board, the head, or the organization well.

David believed he would have benefited from a transition that included the search consultant continuing to work with the head, the search committee, and the board for the ensuing few months following the selection of the candidate. Further, he was certain any nonprofit organization would be well-served to retain the search consultant for an appropriate transition period.

Lesson 2: *Executive sessions are destructive to the relationship between the head and the board.* David was aware that this was a controversial topic, but having experienced this, he strongly believed that such sessions should only be held to evaluate the head. Anything else gave the unmistakable impression that the head and board were not partners in moving the school forward. If a board insists on conducting executive sessions, it is incumbent on the chair to share a summary of the discussion with the head. David had been very clear on the responsibilities and duties of the board since he had not only been a board member at Sanders but had also served on numerous other boards. All nonprofit organizations probably have to address this matter at some point, and David was convinced that most boards would abandon the executive sessions if they knew how counterproductive they are.

Lesson 3: *Trustees who find themselves in conflict with the administration regarding operational issues must either recuse themselves from the matter or step off the board.* Becoming embroiled in such situations and working in opposition to the administration is completely inappropriate. It is a bullying tactic that should not be tolerated. It is the chair's responsibility to not allow such behavior to exist. It is certainly a topic for discussion at the board's orientation session. To David, this was another example of where the organization needed leadership from the board chair. What is operational and what is strategic is clear. In disputes, it is the chair who must demonstrate leadership.

Lesson 4: *Bullying on the part of board members is a disease that must be addressed by the chair.* Most schools have policies and/or statements in their student handbooks about bullying and how administrators will take serious measures to deal with it, so it's absurd to see bullying go undetected or ignored when it happens among board members. The inability to encourage a positive relationship between the head and senior administrators and the board can have devastating consequences. Again, the head of the school or organization CEO and the chair must work together to squelch bullying. It is incumbent on the board's committee on trustees that they work to ensure that anyone who is known for bullying behavior not be considered for the board.

Lesson 5: *Serious discussions are a necessary part of life, but severe, abusive complaints and criticism are usually unwarranted and often destructive.* Because some board members had no boundaries when it came to what they believed they should know, David witnessed firsthand this avenue through which board members attempted to bully and threaten people. While David communicated many issues under the "no surprise" banner, on numerous occasions board members wanted to know more and were convinced that it was their responsibility to know. Some just could not stand it if a question was asked that they could not answer. "You are a board member," they'd hear, "so aren't you supposed to know *everything* that's going on?"

Lesson 6: *Secret board meetings demonstrate the worst possible behavior.* Nothing revealed the complete lack of trust and respect between the head and the board more than for the board to meet in secret. It was an obvious reflection of the lack of partnership that existed. If issues or concerns existed between the head and board, they should have been addressed directly. Keeping secrets from the head or CEO was inappropriate unless the reason was to discuss a specific concern regarding this person.

Lesson 7: *Allowing board members to badly treat the head and other administrators suggests a lack of leadership on the part of the chair.* One of the primary responsibilities of the chair is to work closely with the board, and that includes providing the necessary oversight when they step out of line. Most people do not enjoy confrontation but there are times when addressing difficult situations with senior staff is critical, whether done collectively, individually, or both. The ability to discipline board members when such action is called for is a necessary part of what the chair must do.

Lesson 8: *Once a process has been established and decisions made, reversing a decision because someone simply disagrees is unacceptable.* It is not the prerogative of any board member individually to revisit a decision already made, meet in the absence of the head, and cause disorder by insisting the board take up a matter already resolved. Unless there are extenuating circumstances, such matters should never resurface. Anytime the board reverses an operational decision made by the head, you are asking for trouble. In David's experience, because he was not entrusted to make decisions regarding school uniform changes, he quickly discovered the very troubled relationship between the head and the board.

Lesson 9: *No board member is exempt from giving something to fundraising efforts of the school.* David had served on many boards, and he believed it was an absolute given that board members of a nonprofit organization provide some level of financial support. Everyone did not have the same capacity to give, but everyone did have *some* capacity to be philanthropic. David experienced board members who refused to give because they did not get their way on some issue. David believed if you are mad about something, you need to get over it and get on board with supporting the organization. It was obvious that some thought it was all about them—their agenda. Board members not contributing stood as another reflection of the leadership of the board. The ability to inspire board members enough to give was a quality needed by the chair or the chair of the development committee.

Lesson 10: *Term limits are a useful and a vital attribute of an effective board.* Having board members who were on the board twenty or more years was typically not an effective way to operate. David knew there was the occasional exception to this rule, but all too often long-term members were not especially active, not the best givers, and often had outdated ideas about the operation of the organization. Bylaws that include language about term limits and specific terms for each board member are preferred. There are circumstances when there are individuals whom you believe are needed to retain a certain stature and presence. Be innovative and create an association of former board members, or some other entity on which they can serve.

Lesson 11: *It is critical that the head be a part of the process of selecting new trustees.* There are many characteristics that make for a good, effective trustee. At or near the top of the list would have to be attitude. David believed it was absolutely necessary to discern the attitude of a prospective trustee by discussing with him or her hypothetical situations that a board might regularly face. How this person reacted to the situation would go a long way in determining whether or not he or she would be a board member who understood the individual, unique roles of board members, head of school, and staff.

Lesson 12: *Always remember why you got into this profession.* At an independent school, it's all about the students and their experience. Compliments are few, and when the work that you and your colleagues do is noticed, spread the word and share the good news. Trustees may find no reason to express their appreciation, but there will be others who will let you know that you have made a positive difference in the life of their son or daughter. Cherish and appreciate these moments because they will most likely inspire you to persevere.

Lesson 13: *Trust and respect are characteristics that must be at the core of all relationships.* You are fortunate if you have this; if not, do all you can to develop trust and respect. Being the head of a school or the director of a nonprofit organization presents enormous challenges. The opportunity to work with those for whom trust and respect is central will make the task all that much easier. If trustees do not value what you do, do not see what you are trying to accomplish, and do not believe in your leadership, then it is time to make a change.

Lesson 14: *It is not the responsibility of the board to address concerns parents bring to them.* One of the biggest challenges

David had was trying to convince the board that this was not their responsibility. The issue was often difficult because some trustees were also parents of students, and when other parents approached them with problems, they felt a personal responsibility to solve them. Trustees must be able to distinguish between their role as a trustee and their role as a parent. It is a persistent challenge—but one that is worthwhile.

Lesson 15: *Staff members who complain to a board member without first trying to resolve the issue internally may be guilty of insubordination.* Trustees taken into confidence on these matters should inform the head regarding any such conversation. Withholding this information from the head is completely improper and directly reflects a lack of trust, respect, and partnership. David realized there were those who disagreed with him, but he knew through experience how toxic an environment could become if insubordination was not handled properly. If a staff member believes there is no other recourse but to approach a trustee, that may be a different issue. However, if the head has given no reason for this, it is imperative that the trustee bring the issue to the head.

Lesson 16: *Trustees who expect special treatment or make intrusive requests do not provide the proper leadership needed to move the school or organization forward.* These trustees are interested in their own agendas. Attempting to influence decisions that have no relationship to board responsibilities is a distraction and takes up the time of the head. Trustees have no business inserting themselves into decisions about disciplinary or honor code violations. Furthermore, the attitude of "you need to know how I feel" or "you need my input before you make a decision" suggests a lack of trust in the head's ability to make decisions. What the trustees need to know will be communicated. Anything beyond that is unwarranted.

Lesson 17: *Effective, enlightened, and inspired leadership makes all the difference in the world.* Never was a statement more telling than what David had witnessed and experienced for several years. What could have been an incredible and rewarding experience was for the most part a nightmare. Leaders who ignore their responsibilities—both board and staff—are guilty of creating an atmosphere that is harmful to the school.

Lesson 18: *The head or the appropriate staff should always make personnel decisions.* The board's role is strategic—trustees may have a voice regarding how a hire may impact the budget, but attempting to influence or undermine the hiring process suggests they have forgotten that their only employee is the head or CEO. When the chair steps in to support the head in this process, it reflects an understanding of the importance of trust and respect.

Lesson 19: *There are essential characteristics that must be present to ensure a healthy relationship between the board chair and the head of the school.* David discovered that in the presence of the following seven characteristics all issues, challenges, debates, and disagreements can be addressed in a manner that reveals the best possible outcome:

- Communication and collaboration
- Respect
- Trust
- Support
- Shared vision
- Attitude
- Leadership

Lesson 20: *The chair of the board should not represent extremes in philosophy or action.* Finding a balance is the most effective way to govern. The chair must acknowledge that, from a financial perspective, those who are builders (revenue generators) and those who are cost-cutting extremists (bean counters) must find common ground when addressing issues. What is best for the school? This should be the chief concern and the priority.

Chapter 23

THE VALUE OF CONSENSUS AND TEAMWORK

"We have committed the Golden Rule to memory;
let us now commit it to life."

—*Edwin Markham*

The issue of how a board of trustees carries out its work is one that impacts the organization in significant ways. The principles of teamwork, trust, and partnership are central ones. Ongoing discussions about individuals doing a better job of working together will help focus attention on the strategic work of the board and produce very positive, productive results.

Through conversations with school and nonprofit leaders, as well as trustees, David discovered that many of the decisions made by trustees are made by consensus. He wondered, *Why is this the case, and why is this an effective way to lead and govern?* The value of teamwork cannot be overemphasized. The importance of working together to resolve differences and reach consensus is an important aspect of the best leadership.

After further reflection on the issue, David developed the following list of ten reasons why consensus and teamwork is the most productive way in which to resolve issues:

1. Define what consensus is and is not. Consensus has to do with the general agreement on a particular issue. It should not infer that the agreement has been reached without discussion.

2. The value of consensus is that it amplifies the most important characteristics that define the CEO and board relationship: communication and collaboration. Are we working together for common goals and to ensure the viability of the organization?

3. Consensus builds support among board members. The opportunity to encourage open discussion on a particular topic has the effect of building enthusiasm and a more positive response.

4. Think advisory. While a board certainly has fiduciary responsibilities for the organization, many discussions and decisions are more advisory in their nature and impact. Providing advice and counsel and reaching a

decision by consensus may be more helpful than the need for a formal vote.

5. Consensus is another way to describe teamwork. When the board and CEO are "on the same page," there is a sense of shared vision, common purpose, a pulling together in a direction that is positive and productive.

6. Treating one another with respect will result in working together, and working together will result in building a stronger organization.

7. Working toward consensus may reflect compromise but does so in the best sense of the word.

> When the board and CEO are "on the same page," there is a sense of shared vision, common purpose, a pulling together in a direction that is positive and productive.

8. It's not all about one person. While an individual board member may believe he or she has a compelling agenda, the ability to listen to other perspectives demonstrates a willingness to believe other ideas may be just as valid.

9. There is strength in the concept of servant leadership. Leading by serving suggests an organization that values putting the organization above self.

10. The Golden Rule is golden for a reason. Our objective should be to treat (and work with) others as we want to be treated!

David was confident this list would generate healthy conversation among board members of any organization. He had learned much from his experiences over the years, but one theme in particular seemed to emerge regularly and to have significant consequences: a brighter future requires governing boards and CEOs to work more closely together than ever before. Nonprofit organizations are vital to society and integrated into the fabric of our culture. Indeed they extensively impact the way we live, and their importance and value will only continue to grow.

Chapter 24

EVALUATION
AND COMMUNICATION

"Some men see things as they are and ask why. Others
dream of things that never were and ask why not?"
—GEORGE BERNARD SHAW

Once David had created his list of lessons learned, he had to
figure out how to put them into practice. What strategies and
insights could be gained by this knowledge? And, ultimately, could
there be a new model for governance—a new relationship or partnership that could be forged to advance schools and organizations?

He knew much had been written about board evaluation and
that there are numerous ways in which to measure effectiveness,
but did such measurements truly identify issues regarding the

relationship between the governing board and the head or non-profit CEO? He wondered what questions needed to be asked to ensure genuinely helpful issues were addressed. David determined that there were ten key questions that any board must address to begin the process of building the strongest possible alliance.

1. What is the attitude of each board member on advancing the mission of the school and working in partnership with the leadership?

2. What is the attitude of the collective board toward building the most positive relationship possible between the head and senior leadership?

3. Does every board member understand and demonstrate his or her knowledge of best practices when it comes to appropriate behavior?

4. Is the board leadership (chair) willing and able to discipline board members who do not act in the best interest of the school and whose behavior prevents the board from establishing and maintaining a lasting partnership?

5. Does the board support decisions made by the administration and understand that an individual member forcing his or her contradictory opinion upon others suggests a lack of understanding of their role?

6. Is the board willing to speak directly but respectfully with parents who do not follow protocol and go directly to a

board member before communicating a concern to the relevant staff person?

7. Does the board embrace the belief that every board member must make some level of financial contribution that distinctly defines his or her relationship with the school or organization?

8. Does the board (trustees committee or nominating committee) include the head, CEO, and other appropriate staff when discussing recruitment, nomination, and selection of prospective board members?

9. Does the board agree that any member meddling (interfering in operational issues), bullying, or threatening the school's leadership in one way or another is not only unacceptable but must be addressed directly?

10. Though passionate discussions and even disagreements are acceptable, does the board believe that a member hijacking the agenda or attempting to act out of extremism and self-interest is completely unacceptable?

The challenge then becomes, how do you raise these issues with prospective or even current board members? An environment in which the board declares that what we do and how we act is in the best interest of the organization. It is the board that needs to say, "Recognizing our role as the governing body, we will set aside individual differences and accept our responsibility to serve to the best of our ability and work in partnership with the leadership of the organization."

> It is the board that needs to say, "Recognizing our role as the governing body, we will set aside individual differences and accept our responsibility to serve."

Any evaluation of the board must, in part, be based on these issues and on this statement of responsibility. Why? The school or the nonprofit organization is serving a vital part of society. Those who have gone before, those who are there now, and those who will come in the future are all part of something special—making a positive difference.

Chapter 25

TWO BOARD MEMBERS AWAY FROM CHAOS . . . OR TRUE LEADERSHIP

"Civilization begins with order,
grows with liberty, and dies with chaos."
—WILL DURANT

During the eight years David served as head of Sanders Academy, he traveled frequently to attend professional conferences and workshops and to network with many school heads and nonprofit CEOs. His grasp of the relevant issues was extensive, and he had heard about countless stories regarding the relationship between those who served in his role and those who served on the board of trustees. When a board functioned with a high degree of effectiveness, the organization naturally thrived. When an organization struggled, the core problem was generally a lack of leadership—both within the organization as well as on the board.

During many conversations he would hear, "We have a really good board. They understand their role and are very supportive."

But then the question would come, "Under what circumstances would a constructive board become a dysfunctional board?" The answer was always the absence of leadership.

Boards become ineffectual when the process becomes flawed. This is especially true in the way in which the board perpetuates itself. Committees on trustees or nominating committees that falter in their task to recruit the very best board possible throw the organization into chaos. That is why it's imperative for the head or CEO to be directly involved in the process of identifying and recruiting board members.

> Boards become ineffectual when the process becomes flawed. This is especially true in the way in which the board perpetuates itself.

One story that had been shared with David stood out as a warning as to what could happen given a particular set of circumstances. The issue centered on a head of school who had served in that capacity for over a decade. For a variety of reasons, though, in the past year his demeanor had changed and he was becoming less effective in his role. Did he need support from the board to make the necessary changes to regain his effectiveness? Perhaps his time as head of that school was coming to an end. How should the board handle such a situation? One member of the board, and a former board chair, was increasingly concerned that the head's leadership skills were slipping and that this would ultimately lead to a drop in enrollment, a dip in financial support, and growing unrest among trustees and others close to the school.

This board member, Robert Mathis, took a difficult course of action, but one he believed would be in the best interest of all parties involved. What do you do when you believe the head of the school is losing his effectiveness? Robert had been a board member of that school for over five years. David knew him well and believed him to be an individual of integrity and an effective board member. Robert thought the best approach was to initially have a conversation with the current board chair. Did the chair share Robert's concerns? Maybe Robert was misreading the situation and no one else felt the way he did. The conversation with the chair revealed that they, indeed, were on the same page. Would others feel the same way, though? If so, what were the next steps? If not, how would Robert and the chair proceed, believing a change was necessary?

David reflected on Robert's story. The transition to a new head or CEO was stressful under the best of circumstances. The situation in this case was less than ideal. You had a head who appeared to be struggling and two influential and thoughtful board members who believed a change was needed but were unsure about the course of action. Robert decided he would contact a few trustees who would either confirm or reject the way in which he and the board chair thought.

Over the next two weeks Robert communicated with about a third of the trustees. He was surprised that almost everyone had similar concerns regarding the head. Now what? Should Robert encourage the chair to call a secret meeting? That idea did not appeal to Robert. He was opposed to this and thought it would create a precedent he considered unworthy. What about a conversation that would include a few trustees and the head?

In a conversation with Robert, David raised the questions, "What result do you want to accomplish? Do you believe that the head and board could work together to resolve any conflicts with the head staying at the school? Or, do you believe that the head needs to resign?" Robert indicated he believed a change was probably needed. However, he was willing to consider a scenario that had board members working with, coaching, and mentoring the head to prevent a very difficult transition.

While several board members expressed concerns about the head's leadership, in the end they agreed that advocating a resignation was not the correct way to proceed. The board instead established a committee to work with the head on the issues that were a concern to the board. While this approach was effective, three years later the head resigned and moved on to another school.

Was this matter handled well? Was there another, more effective way? It was difficult because the trustees were facing a situation that did not appear to have a simple or straightforward conclusion.

David knew that well-intentioned boards are thoughtful and intentional regarding the way they try to resolve a difficult and controversial situation. Still, many boards are two members away from chaos, and they do not consider the implications of making decisions based on skimpy information and moving forward too quickly. David knew this way of doing business all too well.

Chapter 26

THE GOVERNANCE
PROMISE

**"I like the dreams of the future better than
the history of the past."**
—THOMAS JEFFERSON

T he word *promise* has several definitions or understandings:
(1) to pledge or commit to something profound or significant; (2) to make somebody expect something; and (3) offer
hope of success. As David considered his eight years as Sanders Academy president, he wanted others in the private school
and nonprofit world to gain from his experiences and learn from
his mistakes. He especially wanted to chart a new course and a
new understanding of how best for staff leadership and board

members to move forward with innovative ways for building their relationships. *Maybe, he thought, what was needed was not a complete shift in the relationship of the governing board but rather a recommitment to the ideals on which this relationship was originally based.* As a result of all he knew, all that he had learned, and all that he reflected, he envisioned what he called The Governance Promise—a new day and a new way of working for the good of the organization.

The Governance Promise would be a strategic way of thinking and approaching the relationship with the governing board. It would embrace these characteristics:

Promise 1: An environment where respect and trust would be exhibited and adopted as the only way in which all business between the leadership of the organization and the governing board would be carried out.

Promise 2: A distinctive positive experience in which the organization thrives because of the partnership established.

Promise 3: A welcoming spirit of cooperation in which the needs and priorities of the organization would always triumph over an individual's agenda or self-interest.

Promise 4: A resolve that even under circumstances in which the organization was under pressure to depart from its mission and goals, the relationship between the staff and the governing board would hold fast to working through whatever conflict or crisis they faced.

Promise 5: A culture in which transitions such as those created when a new board chair is appointed are seamless and come with little interruption to the head or CEO or the trustees.

Promise 6: A commitment to be a model school or nonprofit organization reaching for the highest standards of innovation, professionalism, and excellence.

This would be the new standard on which organizations would be based and be judged. All of the elements for this were present. What was mandatory was a belief in something better than the status quo. A belief that in order to be the best you can be, you have to do the best you possibly can do. A new day was around the corner—if people in leadership had the courage to embrace all that was possible.

> The Governance Promise would be a strategic way of thinking and approaching the relationship with the governing board.

For David, he hoped for and was optimistic about this emerging innovation. He had faith in the future and a belief that his eight years as Sanders's head had been for something much greater than he ever imagined. He realized he was both blessed and grateful. What could be better than that? He was ready for the next phase of his career and life as he sought ways in which he could make a difference.

Chapter 27

A MODEL
FOR EVALUATION

"Everything that can be counted does
not necessarily count: everything that counts
cannot necessarily be counted."
—ALBERT EINSTEIN

Over the eight-year span during which David had served
as president of Sanders Academy, he had worked for and
with three different board chairs. Each had very different personalities, backgrounds, and ways in which they viewed their role.
David acknowledged that it was essential for the future of the
school that he find a way to work with these three very different
board leaders. He was not able to do that, though, and accepted

the responsibility for his failure to achieve better relationships. In his mind and in his heart, he had done everything he could to do what was best for the school and build his relationships in that way.

One issue that haunted him was that over the years there had never been what he considered an appropriate way in which to evaluate his leadership and effectiveness. The criteria used had varied widely and was mostly inappropriate and insensitive. All had not included David in the conversation. There was no communication or collaboration about how his evaluation would be conducted.

> David believed there were four factors that apply to all school leaders as well as nonprofit CEOs.

David developed some ideas and concepts about what he believed to be a much more effective model for something that was actually meaningful and helpful. What was the most effective way to place value on leadership, effectiveness, and impact for the head of school? What should count? What should not count? David believed there were four factors that apply to all school leaders as well as nonprofit CEOs:

Factor 1: The board of trustees should create a committee to review the performance of the head. This committee's duties should be included in the language of the organization's bylaws. By doing so the process is validated and is not subject to the whim of a particular board chair or executive committee. The make-up of the committee should be defined as well. It should include the chair, vice-chair, chair of budget and finance, and chair of development. These four individuals represent critical areas of the school in terms of mission, vision, and sustainability.

This step enables all subsequent steps to work having put in place the most effective process possible.

Factor 2: The committee should stipulate which specific areas in the life of the school or nonprofit will be evaluated. Typically these will include such goals as:

1. Meeting or exceeding budget expectations. Whatever the budget goal is for the school, this is an important factor in evaluating performance.

2. Within budget goals lie those areas that impact the budget:

   Enrollment goals for independent schools
   - What are the mutually agreed upon enrollment goals to reach the budget?
   - What are the goals for retention?
   - What are the goals for adding new students?

   Fundraising goals
   - What are the agreed upon goals for all fundraising activities?
   - What are the goals for the annual fund?
   - What are the goals for special events?

   Other financial goals that ensure budget goals are reached
   - How have these goals been reached?

3. Community service goals
   - What leadership roles do you expect the head or CEO to play?

- Do you expect the head or CEO to seek officer positions within community service organizations?
- Do you expect the head or CEO to be an active volunteer in the community?
- If so, what does that look like?

4. Personnel goals
   - Does the board require specific information such as personnel evaluations for the senior leadership team?
   - What specific expectations is the board seeking given the head is the only employee of the board?

5. Academic goals for independent schools
   - Are there expectations regarding student performance?
   - Are there goals relative to such recognition as number of National Merit scholars?
   - What are the expectations regarding student acceptance at selective and highly selective colleges and universities?
   - Are there goals regarding faculty professional development, including advanced degrees?

Factor 3: This committee has the responsibility to describe any issues or subjects it believes will lead to a poor evaluation beyond what is described above. For example, if the committee believes the head or CEO should attend and be visible at certain events and that their absence would be a concern, this should be communicated to the head or CEO.

143

Factor 4: The committee should not be intrusive when it comes to personnel matters beyond those of the head or CEO who has been appointed. The committee should not require the head or CEO to provide any kind of evaluation to the committee or to the board. Personnel matters and the manner in which these are carried out are the responsibility of the head or CEO.

There was also another reality that David believed was needed. If the relationship between the head or CEO and the committee were healthy then a formal evaluation, while a necessary exercise, was not as critical as the ongoing, day-to-day relationship. Such interaction was a much more effective reflection of what was being achieved.

David was not naïve about the way in which he saw his relationships evolve at Sanders. His greatest hope was that these initiatives would spark a dialogue and ongoing discussion about the nature of governing boards and how they can be incredible partners in this relationship. Change may come slowly or may never happen. However, raising questions and identifying issues are worthwhile when our world's future is at stake.

Appendix A

THE GOVERNANCE PROMISE

The Governance Promise is a strategic way of thinking and approaching the relationship between the head of school/ CEO and the governing board. It should embrace the following characteristics:

- An environment where respect and trust would be exhibited and adopted as the only way in which all business between the leadership of the organization and the governing board would be carried out.

- A distinctive positive experience in which the organization thrives because of the partnership established.

- A welcoming spirit of cooperation in which the needs and priorities of the organization would always triumph over an individual's agenda or self-interest.

- A resolve that even under circumstances in which the organization was under pressure to depart from its mission and goals, the relationship between the staff and the governing board would hold fast to working through whatever conflict or crisis they faced.

- A culture in which transitions such as those created when a new board chair is appointed are seamless and come with little interruption to the head or CEO or the trustees.

- A commitment to be a model school or nonprofit organization reaching for the highest standards of innovation, professionalism, and excellence.

Appendix B

10 KEY QUESTIONS
FOR EVERY BOARD

The following questions are vital to any board that wants to build the strongest possible alliance.

1. What is the attitude of each board member on advancing the mission of the school and working in partnership with the leadership?

2. What is the attitude of the collective board toward building the most positive relationship possible between the head and senior leadership?

3. Does every board member understand and demonstrate his or her knowledge of best practices when it comes to appropriate behavior?

4. Is the board leadership (chair) willing and able to discipline board members who do not act in the best interest of the school and whose behavior prevents the board from establishing and maintaining a lasting partnership?

5. Does the board support decisions made by the administration and understand that an individual member forcing his or her contradictory opinion upon others suggests a lack of understanding of their role?

6. Is the board willing to speak directly but respectfully with parents who do not follow protocol and go directly to a board member before communicating a concern to the relevant staff person?

7. Does the board embrace the belief that every board member must make some level of financial contribution that distinctly defines his or her relationship with the school or organization?

8. Does the board (trustees committee or nominating committee) include the head, CEO, and other appropriate staff when discussing recruitment, nomination, and selection of prospective board members?

9. Does the board agree that any member meddling (interfering in operational issues), bullying, or threatening the school's leadership in one way or another is not only unacceptable but must be addressed directly?

10. Though passionate discussions and even disagreements are acceptable, does the board believe that a member hijacking the agenda or attempting to act out of extremism and self-interest is completely unacceptable?

Appendix C

20 LESSONS
TO LEARN AND TO SHARE

The following are twenty ideas for leading a better independent school or nonprofit organization. Learn them. Live them. Then share them with your team as well as leaders in other organizations. These twenty lessons will have an incredible impact on your board and the entire organization.

Lesson 1: *The search committee must be unanimous in its decision to hire someone.*

Search consultants must communicate as clearly as possible that the search committee ultimately stands behind the majority's decision regardless of the outcome of the initial voting. Otherwise they must resign from the board if they feel they will not be able to support the candidate selected.

Lesson 2: *Executive sessions are destructive to the relationship between the head and the board.*

Such sessions should only be held to evaluate the head. Anything else gives the unmistakable impression that the head and board are not partners in moving the school forward.

Lesson 3: *Trustees who find themselves in conflict with the administration regarding operational issues must either recuse themselves from the matter or step off the board.*

Becoming embroiled in such situations and working in opposition to the administration is completely inappropriate, and it is the chair's responsibility to not allow such behavior to exist.

Lesson 4: *Bullying on the part of board members is a disease that must be addressed by the chair.*

Encourage a positive relationship between the head and senior administrators and the board can have devastating consequences. It is incumbent on the board's committee on trustees that they work to ensure that anyone who is known for bullying behavior not be considered for the board.

Lesson 5: *Serious discussions are a necessary part of life, but severe, abusive complaints and criticism are usually unwarranted and often destructive.*

Although some members believe they need to know everything, the board must not allow them to threaten or bully people in order to get the information they want. It's okay for a board member to not know the answer to every question.

Lesson 6: *Secret board meetings demonstrate the worst possible behavior.*

Nothing reveals the complete lack of trust and respect between the head and the board more than for the board to meet in secret. If issues or concerns exist between the head and board, they should be addressed openly and directly. Keeping secrets from the head or CEO is inappropriate unless it's necessary to discuss a specific concern regarding this person.

Lesson 7: *Allowing board members to badly treat the head and other administrators suggests a lack of leadership on the part of the chair.*

Most people do not enjoy confrontation, but there are times when addressing difficult situations with senior staff is critical, whether done collectively, individually, or both. The ability to discipline board members when such action is called for is a necessary part of what the chair must do.

Lesson 8: *Once a process has been established and decisions made, reversing a decision because someone simply disagrees is unacceptable.*

Unless there are extenuating circumstances, matters that have been voted on and settled should never resurface. There will be trouble any time a board reverses an operational decision made by the head.

Lesson 9: *No board member is exempt from giving something to fundraising efforts of the school.*

Although everyone on a board does not have the same capacity to give, everyone does have some capacity to be philanthropic. It should be an absolute given that board members of a nonprofit organization provide some level of financial support.

Lesson 10: *Term limits are a useful and a vital attribute of an effective board.*

All too often long-term members are not especially active, not the best givers, and often have outdated ideas about the operation of the organization. Bylaws that include language about term limits and specific terms for each board member are preferred.

Lesson 11: *It is critical that the head be a part of the process of selecting new trustees.*

It is absolutely necessary for the head or CEO to discern the attitude of a prospective trustee by discussing with him or her hypothetical situations a board might regularly face. How a person reacts to such scenarios will help build a team that is single-minded in its efforts to build a healthy, growing organization.

Lesson 12: *Always remember why you got into this profession.*

At an independent school, it's all about the students and their experience—even when work goes unnoticed and compliments are few. When you hear what a difference you are making, cherish and appreciate these rare moments and allow them to inspire you to persevere.

Lesson 13: *Trust and respect are characteristics that must be at the core of all relationships.*

The opportunity to work with those for whom trust and respect is central will make the task all that much easier. If trustees do not value what you do, do not see what you are trying to accomplish, and do not believe in your leadership, then it is time to make a change.

Lesson 14: *It is not the responsibility of the board to address concerns parents bring to them.*

Difficulties arise when parents approach board members with problems—especially when those board members are also parents of students. Trustees must be able to distinguish between their role as a trustee and their position as a parent.

Lesson 15: *Staff members who complain to a board member without first trying to resolve the issue internally may be guilty of insubordination.*

Trustees taken into confidence on these matters should inform the head regarding any such conversation. Withholding this information from the head is completely improper and directly reflects a lack of trust, respect, and partnership.

Lesson 16: *Trustees who expect special treatment or make intrusive requests do not provide the proper leadership needed to move the school or organization forward.*

The attitude of "you need to know how I feel" or "you need my input before you make a decision" suggests a lack of trust in the head's ability to make decisions. What the trustees need to know will be communicated. Anything beyond that is unwarranted.

Lesson 17: *Effective, enlightened, and inspired leadership makes all the difference in the world.*

It doesn't take much to turn what could be an incredible and rewarding experience into a nightmare. Leaders who ignore their responsibilities—both board and staff—are guilty of creating an atmosphere that is harmful to the school.

Lesson 18: *The head or the appropriate staff should always make personnel decisions.*

The board's role is strategic—trustees may have a voice regarding how such a hire may impact the budget, but attempting to influence or undermine the hiring process suggests they have forgotten that their only employee is the head or CEO.

Lesson 19: *There are essential characteristics that must be present to ensure a healthy relationship between the board chair and the head of the school.*

All issues, challenges, debates, and disagreements can be addressed in a manner that reveals the best possible outcome when done so in the presence of these seven characteristics: communication and collaboration; respect; trust; support; shared vision; attitude; and leadership.

Lesson 20: *The chair of the board should not represent extremes in philosophy or action.*

Finding a balance is the most effective way to govern. The chair must acknowledge that, from a financial perspective, those who are builders (revenue generators) and those who are cost-cutting extremists (bean counters) must find common ground when addressing issues.

BUILDING
THE IDEAL PARTNERSHIP

It is clear to everyone when a head or CEO connects and communicates effectively with the board chair. An ideal relationship and partnership moves organizations forward, and a "lack of conflict" between two leaders immensely benefits the entire organization. The following are characteristics that will make this relationship so effective:

1. **Communication and collaboration.** *The idea of working together is a key ingredient to success.*

2. **Respect.** *Respect one another, and be aware of each other's capabilities and desire to work hard.*

3. **Trust.** *From respect comes trust, so secret meetings and clandestine communications are unnecessary.*

4. **Support.** *You may disagree on an issue or how to resolve a concern, but don't ever tolerate unprofessional and unethical behavior from any board member.*

5. **Shared vision.** *Success comes when the ultimate reason for any decision is to make the organization better.*

6. **Attitude.** *Surround yourselves with people who want to do things the right way, and then build upon those positive relationships.*

7. **Leadership.** *Lead by example and through serving—and surround yourselves with incredibly talented and capable people you can support.*

Appendix E

WARNING SIGNS

Use this list of warning signs to help you recognize when someone is putting self or another chosen individual's interests above the organization:

1. **Trustees** who allow the business they do together outside of the boardroom to influence the decisions they make inside of it.

2. **Trustees** who allow issues that are not appropriate to discuss in the boardroom, using the venue to perpetuate their agenda.

3. **Trustees** who demand their way on a range of issues and threaten to withhold support if their "demands" are not met.

4. **Trustees** who use their position on the board to obtain business opportunities or recognition without concern as to how it may impact the board and organization.

5. **Trustees** who meet in secret and maintain that such actions are part of what is necessary, claiming such unsanctioned meetings are appropriate.

6. **Trustees** who bully the organization's leadership without regard to the professional and personal damage it causes.

ACKNOWLEDGMENTS

The process of writing this book and telling David's story has not been an easy one. It has been the result of over twenty-five years of experience in school and nonprofit leadership and almost a year of writing. My hope is that the issues and challenges identified in this book will shine a light on the importance of the relationship between the leadership of the organization and its governing board. Schools and nonprofit organizations are a vital part of our culture and have helped shape our society back to the very beginning of this nation. The stakes are simply too high not to make every possible effort to get it right.

When I began this project I was aware that there were many books and articles about all manner of issues regarding the governing board. My purpose was not to repeat what had been done but to take a road less traveled and tell the story of David Andrews and how he coped with and eventually came to terms with the circumstances in which he found himself. His story is a universal one—one with which many can identify. I hope his message strikes a chord with you.

There are many to thank. The process of writing a book is

a collaborative one and there have been many people who have been enormously supportive and helpful.

First, I want to express appreciation to the many school, nonprofit, and board leaders I spoke with and interviewed. Their stories and contributions to *The Board Game* have been incredible and I am deeply grateful for their input.

Next I would like to thank all of those who went to the Web site to complete the survey. Your responses were enormously helpful. In many and important ways, all of the people whom I have encountered and interacted with have helped make this book possible.

Early in the process I sought the advice and support of two people who helped bring perspective and direction to this process. They were both encouraging and realistic as to how this might unfold. I am grateful to Mike Stafford and Lauron Sonnier for being such a valuable and understanding resource when I needed them.

The process of editing is probably a painful one. Therefore I have no doubt that I have caused my wonderful, patient editor much pain. I am truly indebted to Kyle Olund who has made this book much better, clearer, and easier to read than it would have been otherwise. Thanks, Kyle, for helping me bring this project to life.

In addition to Kyle, I would also like to express my appreciation to Dan Wright. Dan's marketing and public relations expertise has been enormously helpful in getting the word out about *The Board Game*. His guidance and wise counsel is deeply appreciated. If you are reading this, then it is probably due to the fact that Dan knew how to get it into your hands.

My parents, Charles and Edith Mott, have been a tremendous source of inspiration, and I am indebted to them. They raised both my brother and me to try to make a positive difference in the world, and they led by example. My brother, Mike, passed away a few years ago, but his legacy along with that of my parents' has made an indelible mark on me.

Over thirty years ago I completed my doctoral dissertation. In that publication I expressed gratitude to my fiancé who a few months later became my wife. Amazingly, she is still with me. This book is dedicated to Courtney Mott. Her faith in me has spanned more than three decades. I am grateful for her support, encouragement, and unfailing belief in me. My universe may be a small one, but she is at its center. The book is also dedicated to our two children—Courtney Leigh and Robert. Both Courtney and I are enormously proud of them. They are our heroes!

ABOUT THE AUTHOR

As a consultant, speaker, teacher, and author, William R. Mott, Ph.D., has assisted hundreds of organizations; these include many independent schools, colleges, museums, libraries, churches, and nonprofits with governance, fundraising, marketing, and management. Dr. Mott is an expert in all aspects of board governance issues and challenges.

In addition to his consulting, Dr. Mott is also the Coordinator of the Master of Organizational Leadership (MOL) Program with an emphasis in Independent School Leadership at Trevecca Nazarene University in Nashville, Tennessee. This program is designed for anyone working in independent schools, providing an opportunity to expand their skills, knowledge, and opportunities for career advancement.

Under his leadership Dr. Mott has conducted numerous capital campaigns, successfully enhancing many annual fund and membership programs. Even during an economic downturn, organizations have turned to Dr. Mott to achieve double-digit increases in annual giving.

His focus is on governance issues, specifically the connection between nonprofit boards and their organizations' senior leadership. Working with boards to deepen their relationship with the whole organization is central to his efforts. *The Board Game*, in conjunction with his blog (at williamrmottphd.com) and workshops, reflects this concentration.

Your organization will benefit from Dr. Mott's vast experience. He has served as a director of development for a major university, executive director of a museum house, president of a college, head (president) of two independent schools, and for eleven years served as president of his own consulting firm.

Dr. Mott holds a Ph.D. in educational leadership from Vanderbilt University's Peabody College. Peabody is noteworthy as the number one college of education in the country, according to *U.S. News & World Report*, for the last three years.

He and his wonderful wife, Courtney, have been married for more than thirty-two years. They are the proud parents of Robert and Courtney Leigh.

THE

BOARD GAME

We invite you to continue your experience
with *The Board Game* at:
WilliamRMottPhD.com or **TheBoardGameCoach.com**

If you have enjoyed *The Board Game* and believe its message has been beneficial, please consider these ideas:

- Engage Dr. Mott to facilitate a retreat for the Board of Trustees using the book as the resource material.
- Engage Dr. Mott to conduct your orientation session for new trustees.
- Play the Board Game! Dr. Mott has created an interactive game based on the issues raised in his book. This game is ideal for board retreats, orientation sessions, and other board training opportunities.
- Buy ten copies of the book and give them to people you think this book will help.
- Create small discussion groups using issues raised in the book.
- Share the book with your friends on Facebook, LinkedIn, and Twitter.

For additional information about having the author
speak to your organization or group, please visit:

WilliamRMottPhD.com or TheBoardGameCoach.com.

PERSONAL REFLECTIONS
AND ACTION STEPS

As you read through this book, highlighting sections that are incredibly relevant to you and your current situation, use these blank pages to write out your thoughts and to create a game plan that will help bring about impactful and lasting changes in your organization.

PERSONAL REFLECTIONS AND ACTION STEPS

PERSONAL REFLECTIONS AND ACTION STEPS

PERSONAL REFLECTIONS AND ACTION STEPS

PERSONAL REFLECTIONS AND ACTION STEPS

PERSONAL REFLECTIONS AND ACTION STEPS